THE GREAT BRITISH
OBSESSION

FRANCIS WILSON

JARROLD

THE GREAT BRITISH OBSESSION
Designed and produced by Parke Sutton Limited, Norwich,
for Jarrold Publishing, Norwich.

First Edition Copyright © Jarrold Publishing 1990
Text Copyright © Francis Wilson 1990

ISBN: 0-7117-0523-2

Printed in Great Britain
Text typeface 10pt Rockwell Light

THE GREAT BRITISH
OBSESSION

The BBC TV Weatherman
FRANCIS WILSON

JARROLD

Contributors

AUTHOR
Francis Wilson

EDITOR
Sarah Whittley

DESIGNER
Gillian Matthews

RESEARCHER
Jan Tavinor

*and with thanks to
Punch Publications Ltd.*

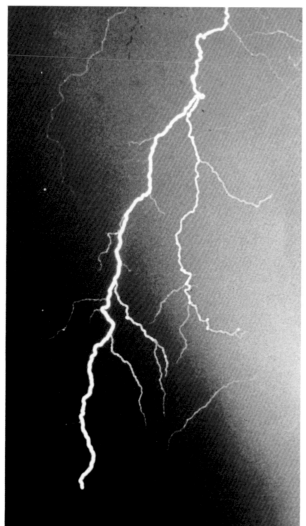

CONTENTS

PART OF OUR LIVES

When two Englishmen meet, their first talk is of the weather.

Samuel Johnson, *The Idler*

A CRUMB OF COMFORT.

JONATHAN. "THEY *DU* SAY WE SENT YOU THIS DARN'D WEATHER! DON'T KNOW 'BOUT THAT!
ANYHOW, I GUESS WE'LL SEND YOU THE CORN!!"
FARMER BULL. "THANK'EE KINDLY, JONATHAN, BUT I'D RATHER HA' DONE WITHOUT BOTH!!!"

Next time a bottle of wine is uncorked, pause and wonder what it was that ripened the grapes that gave us the wine. Imagine the sharp winter nights, the soaking rains, the exhilarating blue skies and the balmy harvest days. The grapes could so easily have been wiped out through drought, flood, frost, hail, pests – for all sorts of reasons. To a grape, what the atmosphere does is a matter of life or death – and we breathe that same atmosphere. Our breath goes into other plants. The food chain takes it on to another person; we are all made of the same substance. The atmosphere is our common bond. What the atmosphere does – its weather – is a common bond between people all over the world. Some people can go through life and be too busy to find out about weather. Others though – and in Great Britain they are in the majority – take a great interest in weather. In fact it is the *great British obsession.*

'Everyone talks about the weather, but nobody does anything about it' was how Charles Warner put it. A Scottish lady I overheard at a bus stop during a heavy shower put it another way: 'Don't knock the weather – most folk could-nee start a conversation if it didnee change once in a while.' Presumably she was saying that because weather is so pervasive, such a common bond between us all, everyone can respond to a comment about the weather. No one can be offended by the weather, and it helps break the ice that sometimes exists. Her opinions held water.

Everyone of course sees weather slightly differently, but all agree that life is richer for it.

We all discuss it at some time or other, and we all complain about it too. The great propensity for the British to grumble about the weather is well known. When at long last we have hot sunshine, everyone worries about a drought; and when we have plenty of rain, 'It's always raining in Britain.'

The painters Turner and Constable could not have grumbled much. On their canvases they captured the true magnificence and unceasing activity of the aerial envelope of weather. They could see the soft and pure melody of the glowing dawn, the turrets and towers of the storm, and the fantastic fragments of blazoned red at sunset. During the early 1800s there was a lot of volcanic activity around the world; this in turn put a vast amount of dust into the atmosphere which meant that amazingly colourful sunsets were enjoyed by all and painted by Turner. The paintings remind us all that the weather is a truly wondrous sight, with many a view of extraordinary splendour and beauty. Many a poet also tried to fathom the mysterious laws of nature.

In his lone course the shepherd oft
*   will pause*
And strive to fathom the mysterious laws
By which the clouds, arranged in
*   light or gloom*
On Mona settle and shapes assume
Of all her peaks and ridges.

Traditional

Right Grapes like these grew in abundance in medieval Britain and may well do so again as global warming takes effect during the next century.

Left Petworth Park: Tillington Church in the Distance painted by Joseph M W Turner in 1828. Turner's vivid and turbulent skies were a result of volcanic activity around the world at this time. The dust thrown into the atmosphere created amazing sunsets and cloud formations.

Below Hampstead Heath with a Rainbow by John Constable in 1836. This painter, usually known for his gentle country landscapes must also have been influenced by the dramatic skies.

We talk about it, we complain about it, and we like to think we can predict it, even though the only thing that is predictable about the weather is that it is unpredictable – such are the vicissitudes of British weather. But then it is the unexpected change in the weather that keeps us human. Despite a sudden drenching, it is entirely human and endearing to be found singing in the rain. The title song from the film *Singing in the Rain*, with its brilliant dance sequence, won the hearts and sentiments of millions.

Right Gene Kelly in the film *Singing in the Rain*, happily dancing underneath the Hollywood hosepipes!

Far left A profusion of hollyhocks in a picturesque English country garden.

Above Fortunately this snowy desolate scene could never be found in our current cool temperate climate.

Left In the sun-baked earth of drought-ridden lands the emphasis must be on survival rather than the picturesque.

The unpredictable nature of weather in Britain – set within a climate that is on the whole more or less pretty reliable – is the one thing that every day we talk about, the one thing we all have in common. It is one of the great sweeteners and cements of conversation – so much so that the British have a worldwide reputation for talking about the weather.

Most people are not at all interested in meteorology *per se* – even though it is the most thought provoking of the environmental sciences. The interest that people have is mainly in the daily weather and the effect it will have on their arrangements. We don't always like it, but at least we can take comfort in the thought that many other people may be in an even worse position at the same time. That thought can give some shelter during a passing shower.

It is the weather that brings forth the lovely British gardens. The English country garden is famous throughout the world, and rightly so. What a pleasure to walk bare footed on fresh cut grass – and how the grass grows! Further south towards the equator the soils are a dusty, yellowy red. Those drought ridden lands have a very different weather regime. In the other direction towards the poles lie raw, windswept, lifeless, cold lands that the weather has in its icy grip. People living off those lands have to skimp and scrape, just to survive. Any swing in the weather can drive them to hunger. To them, the weather is a matter of life or death. How lucky we are here in Britain to have our temperate climate. Is not the sight of a country garden quite wonderful? How well it responds to the weather through the seasons.

Above The fate of a typically English fête!

There is something peculiarly British about people with newspapers over their heads rushing for the entrance to the marquee to find others there, shrugging their shoulders and listening to the sound of rain falling on fabric. Events like that stick in the memory and prejudice the mind against the British weather, when in fact it is not so bad. For example, let's say someone cycled to work between eight and nine each morning, no holidays and no weekends off. How many times would our cyclist be soaked in a year? I'd be willing to bet on fewer than a dozen. It is the times we arrive at work drenched that we remember; the rest – the most – are forgotten.

The unexpected drenching is just a necessary consequence of living in our favoured equable climate. The Gulf Stream around our shores effectively ensures that Britain does not suffer the extremes of temperatures that continental places of the same latitudes have to put up with. The Atlantic Ocean effectively modifies any approaching extreme air mass, and this is most often where our weather comes from, as the world goes round west to east. In fact latitude for latitude Britain is the warmest place in the world. Compare for example the Falkland Islands at roughly 50°S, the same latitude as the south of England. Anyone who has been to the Falklands will know that its climate is roughly that of the extreme north of Britain. For this favoured climate of ours we pay a price. The price is more water from the ocean in the approaching air, and consequently always the risk of rain turning up. How many times do we hear on the sports news 'rain stopped play'?

Cricket is a pretty odd game in many ways, but I've never understood why someone should want to play a game that has every chance of being unfairly interfered with by the elements. A one day match is fine, but why do they go on for five days? It is bound to rain at some point, and save the weak side from losing. National teams that play here have more than just our cricket ability to reckon with. It seems grossly unfair that a team on the point of victory should be foiled with just one wicket to go, simply because the skies darken or it rains. Test matches at Old Trafford, Manchester were a complete washout during 1880 and 1938. From the records of all the test matches at Old Trafford the chance of a wet day stopping play is about one match in two. For test matches at the Oval or Lord's the chance is about one match in five. Maybe it is the televising of interrupted Manchester test matches that has reinforced the myth of a rainy city.

The British Isles stretch from the Channel Islands in the south to the Shetland Islands in the north, roughly 600 miles. While the weather keeps the snow lying on the northern hills of Scotland for most of the year, it also nurtures a blaze of flowers all year round on Jersey. As well as a range of weathers across Britain on any one day, the weather at any one place will often change. If you don't like the weather, wait a while. The idea that 'it always rains in Manchester' is quite wrong. The only thing that the weather in Britain always does is change – and it's change that keeps our weather interesting. There's not much point in talking about the weather if it is always dry, sunny and hot. It may be good for a holiday, but eternal holiday weather becomes an eternal bore. A change is as good as a rest.

The fickleness of the British weather adds a certain spice to life. Just when everything seems under control for the most important event of the year, let's say a wedding or the local fête, just when all the arrangements have been made, someone says: 'But what if it rains?' It is now possible to insure against a rainy day, but the premiums are costly. Most of us end up by trying to make an undercover area. The marquee is a familiar sight at nearly all big outdoor events, and has saved the day for many a garden party.

Golf is another game that is extremely weather sensitive as it seems to take so long to finish. I suspect it takes so long because the players fan the ball repeatedly and when they eventually make contact, spend the rest of the day trying to find it again!

One of the great seasonal pleasures is watching Wimbledon. First class tennis is played on lush green grass out in the open, often under dramatic skies. It reminds everyone that summer is back – but it is a British summer. On 2nd July 1980 there was almost unbearable

Above left 4th Test, England v. Australia, Old Trafford 1985. Umpire Dickie Bird removes the stumps: another break for rain!

Above Perhaps the last swing of the day, even the popular golf umbrella would be no defence against these skies.

Left Spectators 'enjoy' another afternoon's tennis at Wimbledon.

THE WASHED-OUT TENNIS-PLAYERS.

(*A Reminiscence of the Rain.*)

(*Chorus.*)—" We're all the way from Belgravia, and we don't know what to do!
We don't know what to do-o-oo! We don't know what to do-o-oo!
We're out of Play, and we're willing to Play—but we've got no Play to do!"

drama in the match between Billie Jean King and Chris Evert. They had reached match point and the game had swung to deuce. Then down came the rain and stopped the match. Yes, that's England. Despite the rain the Wimbledon fortnight has tremendous appeal because of the jolly atmosphere which reigns among the onlookers throughout the whole tournament.

Far from being upset by the elements, for some it is the challenge of man against the elements that makes life worthwhile. There are many ways of getting to the top of a mountain, for example by helicopter, and when you get there the view is always the same. However, mountain climbers deliberately pit themselves against nature, against snowstorms and avalanches, and deliberately test themselves against the mountain, as that time of being so close to earth and nature is something very special to them. In some people there is still an urge to go out and face the elements, to live close to nature. Pot-holers are the same sort of people, willing to take on the earth and the atmosphere – and sometimes with disastrous consequences. An unexpected cloudburst can pour hundreds of tons of water in a matter of minutes down the very hole that the explorers are uncovering. The race against time to get back to the surface, the work of the emergency rescue services to seek and find, the condemnation of mad adventurism, all these are things we see on the news; but behind that lies the fact that man is still linked to the elements. Somewhere deep down and suppressed in most of us are primitive man's vital links with the atmosphere, the earth, the climate and the weather.

Climate and weather were responsible for the evolution of Britain. Some 7000 years back the retreating ice age sheets over the North Sea and Baltic finally melted, causing the sea level to rise so much that the lowlands near southeast England were permanently flooded. The Straits of Dover were formed and Britain was born. In the slowly warming weather the primitive British cave-man hunter came down from the hills to become village man, the food grower.

Settlements breed culture and from culture comes civilisation. The warm weather peaked around 6000 years ago when massive trees were able to grow right across Scotland. Our climate was then similar to today's Dordogne region in the south of France. Early Britons worshipped the warmth from the sun, erecting monuments or primitive solar observatories from Stonehenge to the Orkneys.

By 500 BC the warm period was over and the weather was in decline. Settlements on Dartmoor and the Pennines had to be abandoned and trees disappeared from the highlands while peat bogs formed in the west. Wooden tracks had to be laid to help pass across the Somerset flats, and the whole village of Glastonbury was built on wooden piles. Abroad there were lands free from this downturn in the weather. Greece was one such land. Free from climatic stress, civilisation was developing fast around Athens. The teachings of the Greek philosophers came to dominate Europe's civilisation, democracy and science. The word 'atmosphere' comes from Ατμoś (vapour), and ∑φαιρα (sphere). Aristotle called the science of the atmosphere 'meteorology'.

During the Roman conquest of Britain the wet weather maintained a high water table, so that marching legions could always be sure of water by digging shallow wells.

Warmer weather returned during the 1100s and 1200s. These Middle Ages were a time of plenty. Dartmoor was resettled. Vineyards were a great success over England and Wales as far north as the Pennines. English wine matched French wine for quality and strength, not having May frosts was a major contributory factor. During the 1300s the weather took a downturn

Left A sudden downpour could make pot-holing an even more hazardous pastime.

Below This mysterious monument, completed around 1550 BC was perhaps built as a place of sun worship; the Heel Stone stands on the axis of sunrise at the summer solstice. Although known as a centre of Druid worship, the construction of Stonehenge began almost 3000 years before the Celtic Druids arrived in Britain.

Above *The Armada in the Straits of Dover*, Flemish School, 1588.

Right *Defeat of the Spanish Armada*, a design for a tapestry. It is interesting to note that although Sir Francis Drake is proclaimed a hero, only three ships were sunk as a direct result of his actions, the rest, about 550, were sunk by the weather!

again, producing a string of failed grain harvests and so causing widespread famine and death. Medieval hamlets were abandoned as people took off to look for food. The wet summers allowed ergot blight to contaminate the meagre harvests. Epidemics killed off whole communities. Possibly half the population of Britain was wiped out.

By the 1500s icesheets had spread back to Iceland, turning Greenland (as the Vikings of the 1200s saw it) into a 'whiteland', which it mostly still is today. Permanent snowbeds became commonplace in the Scottish Highlands. The harsh cold period between 1550 and 1850 is known as the Little Ice Age.

The cooling of the north Atlantic sharpened the temperature contrast between equator and pole. This strengthened the atmospheric circulation, producing more severe storms. One such wild storm changed the course of British history. The Spanish Armada set sail early in the summer of 1585, intending to crush the British fleet in the Channel, then pick up the Spanish army in the Netherlands and invade Britain unhindered at Dover. However, they forgot to take into account one of the most essential things – the British weather. First of all they were becalmed and went back to southern Spain. Eventually they got to north-west Spain, but were hit by a storm and had to go back and prepare again. At long last in 1588 the Armada moved into the English Channel, and as fate would have it a severe storm swelled up the Channel, pushing the Armada into the Straits. Francis Drake created even more chaos and havoc by sending in the fire ships. The Armada scattered over a large area. Only one galleon was sunk by cannon fire and just two were damaged by the fire ships, yet the Spanish were defeated because the whole fleet became uncoordinated. The gales kept blowing them northwards and, not wanting to go back to the Straits of Dover, most of the Spanish galleons tried to go round the north of Scotland. Some were blown on to the coast and wrecked, others were blown almost to Iceland. On other galleons, typhoid broke out during the prolonged journey home. About 550 Spanish ships were sunk by the *weather*.

The other famous sea battle, the Battle of Trafalgar, was fought in completely the opposite conditions. The reluctant French and Spanish fleet came out of Cadiz harbour taking full advantage of the sudden northerly wind, hoping to make a run for it to the Straits of Gibraltar some 50 miles south. Nelson had

brilliantly anticipated this and positioned his fleet south of Cadiz and over the horizon. The enemy were spotted heading south by Trafalgar

Left The Battle of Trafalgar, *Crippled but Unconquered,* 1805 by W. L. Wyllie.

Below The Battle of Trafalgar, 21 October, 1805 by J. M. W. Turner. Nelson was aided by the weather as he approached the opposing fleets head on. The light winds delayed the confrontation causing the enemy to lose their nerve and scatter, enabling Nelson to pick them off one by one.

Right The influx of Scottish Protestants to Ulster in the early 17th century was the cause of the Catholic v. Protestant conflict.

a massive scale. Poverty and famine were widespread. King James VI evicted the native Irish from their rich sheltered lands in Ulster and replaced them with immigrant Scottish farmers, forced off their lands by the weather. By 1612 there was a mass migration of Scots to Ulster. This began the Northern Ireland troubles. The 1690s were even worse. The weather in Scotland was very bad, some reports suggested that people were reduced to fighting over edible graveyard nettles. In parts of Scotland more than half the population starved to death. Others migrated to Ulster. A weak and depleted Scotland was finally taken over by England in 1707.

The 1810s and 1820s were the coldest years in Britain since the 1690s had ravaged Scotland. These were the formative years of Charles Dickens, who did much to promote the idea that Christmases should have lots of deep lying snow. This could be due to the fact that six out of Dickens's first eight winters were bitterly cold. In those years white Christmases were the norm. Frost fairs were held on the Thames. They were by all accounts gay, lively and popular events. The theatres lay empty. The ice cover on the Thames was so thick that it could hold enormous wooden structures. The tidal waters underneath pushed up the ice twelve feet, and still it did not break. Today the Thames is rarely below 10°C: the winters are less cold, the new open bridges allow the tide to reach far up the river, the steep embankments concentrate the flow, and contamination effectively warms the water.

The Little Ice Age in Dickens's time came to an end when there were some very warm summers. The summer of 1846 completely changed the course of Irish history. A very warm and exceptionally humid summer in Ireland provided the potato blight fungus with just the right rapid breeding environment. The potato harvest that year was completely contaminated. Since it was the main and sometimes the only food, many Irish folk were either poisoned or starved to death. Today the population of Ireland is roughly half of what it was before the potato famine.

A major turning point in history when the weather was vital was D-Day. For an invasion of France to be successful in pushing back the Germans, it was essential that at the time of invasion there was simultaneously:

- Late moonlight so that the night paratroopers could see what they were up to.

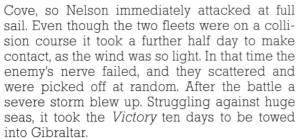

Cove, so Nelson immediately attacked at full sail. Even though the two fleets were on a collision course it took a further half day to make contact, as the wind was so light. In that time the enemy's nerve failed, and they scattered and were picked off at random. After the battle a severe storm blew up. Struggling against huge seas, it took the *Victory* ten days to be towed into Gibraltar.

The cooler weather of the Little Ice age hit Scotland worst of all. Times were very hard in the 1590s. A succession of crop failures caused by the cold, raw, wet weather led to starvation on

- A low dawn tide so that the beach obstacles and mines could be exposed and cleared.

- No low cloud so that the bombers and big naval guns might see what they were aiming at.

- No strong winds so that the troops could get out of their landing craft with their equipment intact.

- And of course lots of luck.

The weather window duly turned up on 6th June 1944 and the invasion was a success.

In more recent times there has been a slow warming of the weather over Britain; there was a peak in the 1930s, and there is a further warming trend at this very moment. Some people will remember how in their youth the summers seemed to be so much warmer. British people today have not really known climatic stress. The 1950s and 1960s were an age of confidence, assurance, getting things done. But the 1970s produced droughts in many parts of the world, massive crop failures and minimal fish catches. The result was worldwide inflation which affected Britain as badly as anywhere else.

Clearly weather and climate down the ages have played a major part in shaping Britain and the British. Primitive Britons lived close

Left The Normandy coast, 6 June 1944, D-Day. As Winston Churchill stated: 'The greatest amphibious operation in history.'

to nature, watched the skies closely and smelt the air. We've come a long way since then, but our fascination with the weather remains.

Our poets down the ages have expressed the emotions it stirs in them.

As far back as the 14th Century our writers were influenced by the wonder of British weather. Geoffrey Chaucer was one such artist.

When in April the sweet showers fall
And pierce the drought of March
*　　to the root, and all*
The veins are bathed in liquor
*　　of such power*
As brings about the engendering
*　　of the flower,*
When also Zephyrus with his sweet breath
Exhales an air in every grove and heath
Upon the tender shoots,
*　　and the young sun*
His half course in the sign of the
*　　Ram has run.*

Geoffrey Chaucer, 'Prologue',
The Canterbury Tales (1387)

Far right Spring is the time of flowers. Usually the snowdrop appears first, followed by in sequence, celandines, primroses, violets, bluebells and of course daffodils. It is said that when a young maiden can put her foot down on seven daisies, spring has arrived.

Right Autumn gives back to earth the leaves that summer lent.

John Keats, who abandoned his medical training for the love of poetry, wrote the famous verse *To Autumn*, which sums up the season so aptly.

Season of mists and mellow fruitfulness
Close bosom-friend of the maturing sun;
Conspiring with him how to
*　　load and bless*
With fruit the vines that round
*　　the thatch-eves run;*
To bend with apples the moss'd
*　　cottage-trees,*
And fill all fruit with ripeness to the core;
To swell the gourd, and plump
*　　the hazel shells*
With a sweet kernel; to set budding more,
And still more, later flowers for the bees,
Until they think warm days
*　　will never cease,*
For Summer has o'er-brimm'd
*　　their clammy cells.*

John Keats, *To Autumn* (1819)

A CALENDAR OF UNUSUAL WEATHER EVENTS

The spring, the summer,
The chiding autumn, angry winter, change
Their wonted liveries and the mazed world
By their increase, now know not which is which.

Shakespeare, *A Midsummer Night's Dream*

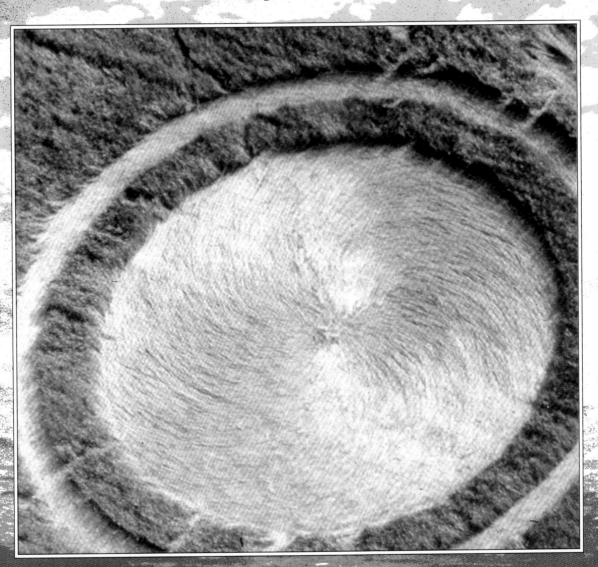

Right Freezing rain can be clear or opaque depending on whether or not the trapped air can escape. If the air can escape then the ice is clear.

JANUARY
Freeze the pot by the fire.

Worst Storm   18th January 1881
Worst snowstorm of the nineteenth century in London, with drifts four and a half metres deep in Oxford Circus, and Fleet Street completely blocked.

Record Pressure   26th January 1884
The lowest ever mean sea level air pressure ever recorded in Britain: 926.5 millibars at the storm centre over Perthshire.

Record Pressure   31st January 1901
The highest air pressure ever recorded in Britain: 1055 millibars at Aberdeen.

Sea Ice   5th January 1928
A storm surge and combined snow thaw forced a sea flood in the Thames. People were drowned in their homes in London.

Ice-Up   27th January 1940
Over Wales and south-west England freezing rain, falling on to subzero land froze over everything it touched. The countryside appeared to be encased in glass. Telegraph poles collapsed under the weight of ice. The ice was so thick and hard that it could only be removed with hammers. Birds could not fly; their wings were glued to their bodies and their feet frozen to the ground. Tree trunks were split to the ground. Traffic was paralysed as car doors froze solid and movement uphill became impossible. The thaw eventually came on 3rd February.

Big Freeze   20th January 1947
The start of the snowiest winter of the twentieth century. By 30th January the snow was 30 centimetres deep over southern England. In February the level snow depth reached 71 centimetres in Durham. The London to Brighton train journey took eight hours instead of one. Drifts of snow in eastern England reached eight metres deep and cut off many villages. Snow fell every day somewhere in the country until 17th March. On 11th March rain in southern England began a rapid thaw. The thaw had spread to the whole country by 22nd March, the subsequent floods turned most areas from Yorkshire to Somerset to Kent into huge lakes. That year in August there was a drought and a heatwave.

Previous page Circles in fields might just be an unusual weather event caused by descending vortices of air that circle and flatten the crops. On the other hand they might be made by merry young farmers!

Storm Surge   31st January 1953
A storm crossed the Orkneys, headed for East Anglia. Gusts of 126 mph were recorded. The storm caused unprecedented destruction of forests over north and east Scotland. The storm surged across the North Sea on 1st February combined with a high soaring tide, inundating 250,000 acres of farmland with salt water. It was the worst ever East Anglian flood disaster.

Big Freeze   January 1963
The big freeze continues from December 1962. From 14th to 26th of January there was no thaw at all in the south of Britain. The big freeze ended in March with a spell of brilliant sunshine. The rains came on 6th March.

100 mph Plus   15th January 1968
The Glasgow 'hurricane'. The wind in Glasgow gusted over 100 mph. Nine people were killed as chimney stacks collapsed in tenement blocks.

Ice Fall   2nd January 1977

A 50 kilogram block of ice, roughly equivalent to two sacks of potatoes, crashed through a roof in Ponders End, Middlesex. Possibly it was a lump of aircraft icing; no one knows.

Tornado Cluster   3rd January 1978

Fourteen tornadoes in all crossed rural parts of eastern England. In one incident 136 geese were sucked up and thrown down dead.

Storm Surge   11th and 12th January 1978

A storm surge caused extensive sea flooding and damage to coastal areas from Humberside southwards. The Thames Barrier at Woolwich was raised for the first time since being built to protect London.

Record Frost   10th January 1982

The coldest air temperature ever recorded in Britain was –27°C at Braemar in the Grampians. On the same night the coldest air temperature ever recorded in England was –26.1°C at Newport.

100 mph Plus   25th January 1990

The third most destructive storm ever to have hit Britain. The storm devastated England and Wales and forty-six people were killed.

Left Clearing the way in East Anglia during the big freeze of 1963. This particular snowdrift was about 400 yards long and up to eight feet deep.

FEBRUARY

February, fill the dyke
With what thou dost like.

Fish Rain   9th February 1859
At Aberdare in Glamorgan it rained minnow and stickleback over a third of an acre.

Red Rain   21st February 1903
Saharan dust fell from dry air over England and Wales. The next day a thick orange fog rolled into Cornwall off the sea.

Record Snow   16th February 1925
The deepest single day's snowfall in Britain, not counting hills above 300 metres, occurred on the south-east fringe of Dartmoor: six feet of snow in fifteen hours.

Cold Swing   1st February 1956
The midday temperature in London was only −4°C, after the previous day's 8°C.

Record Heat   28th February 1959
The highest February air temperature ever recorded: 19°C at Greenwich.

Big Freeze   February 1963
The big freeze goes on. It was the last time the Thames froze over. People could cross by foot above Kingston upon Thames onwards; below that point the excess heat from the power stations kept the river from freezing up.

Red Rain   11th February 1982
Saharan dust fell with rain over the home counties, Hampshire and the Isle of Wight.

Storm Sequence   1st February 1990
Just one week after the storm of 25th January 1990, the fourth most devastating storm hit Britain, while another ravaged Scotland and Northern Ireland. A sequence of major storms had begun. The following storms arrived on 3rd, 7th, 8th and 26th February over various parts of Britain.

Record 1990
February 1990 turned out to be the wettest month on record for the west of Scotland, and the windiest month on record for the south of England. It was also the mildest February for more than 200 years in central England.

Above Workers playtime on the River Wensum in Norwich during the cold spell in 1963.

MARCH

In like a lion, out like a lamb.

Snowstorm   9th March 1891
Great snowstorm covers England. The *Zulu Express* left Paddington on 9th and arrived at Plymouth on 13th after being buried under a snowdrift of four metres.

Late Blizzard   28th March 1916
Blizzards in the south of England blew down trees and telegraph poles and paralysed traffic.

Left Towyn, February 1990. A major storm pounded the sea defences at Towyn on the north coast of Wales. At high tide the Irish Sea flooded the entire town.

Bizarre   10th March 1929
Air temperature reached 21°C, yet there was ice skating in the sunshine on thick ice that had been preserved by the freezing nights in the Lake District.

Record Wind   6th March 1967
Strongest wind gust ever *recorded* in Britain, the gust measured 144 mph at the Cairngorms weather station.

Floods   26th and 27th March 1968
The year of the floods over western Scotland, when 25 centimetres of rain fell in two days.

Red Rain   5th and 6th March 1977
Red rain fell over western Scotland. The origin was probably the Sahara.

APRIL
An April day will suddenly bring showers.

Snowstorm   5th April 1911
A snowstorm blew down the largest tree in Britain: an elm at Oxford.

Earliest Heatwave   16th April 1949
30°C (85°F) in London.

Lightning Strike   8th April 1979
Lightning from a storm at Caerleon, Gwent, struck eleven football players as they left the field. One was critically burnt.

Record Sun   April 1990
The sunniest April ever known over the southern half of Britain.

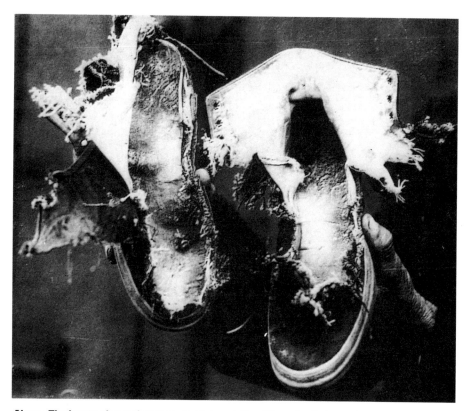

Above The boots of an unfortunate lightning victim; life or death depends on the route of the strike past the vital organs. Lightning could run down a wet coat, missing the body and end up on the shoes. Luckily the strike only lasts a fraction of a second, so some people live to tell the tale.

Right In one single flash of lightning the air can be heated to an incredible 15,000°C. The energy in a summer thunderstorm is probably ten times greater than the energy of the Hiroshima bomb.

MAY

March winds and April showers bring forth May flowers.

Late Snow   27th May 1821
The latest known date of the year for a significant amount of snowfall in the London area.

Record Drought   15th May 1893
The longest absolute drought in Britain ended after seventy-three consecutive rainless days in Mile End, London.

Lightning Strike   31st May 1911
Continuous lightning for several hours killed seventeen people and four horses at the Epsom Derby Day races.

Cloudburst   29th May 1920
People were drowned in their homes near Louth, Lincolnshire and £100,000 worth of damage done by a freak cloudburst.

Record High   22nd May 1922
Earliest date for the shade air temperature reaching 33°C in London.

Fish Rain   29th May 1928
Over Comber, Ireland it rained a shower of sea fish.

Record Frost   16th May 1935
A record sharp May frost of −12°C at Rickmansworth, Buckinghamshire.

THE WET DERBY

BOB BRABAZON DOES NOT THINK IT SUCH A *VERY* BAD DAY!

THE NEW UMBRELLA

FOR AVOIDING BORES.

FOR PROTECTING THE TROUSERS.

FOR PURE ALTRUISM.

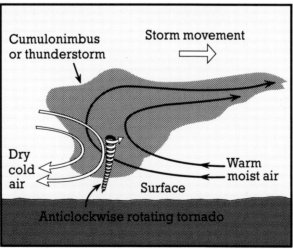

Above Tornadoes originate within the cloud and like an elephant's trunk dip down to the ground. The extreme low pressure in the centre of the tornado causes all the damage. The worst tornado in Britain was on 28th December 1879, the Tay bridge collapsed and 75 people were lost in the Firth.

Vertical section through the parent storm of a tornado. A tornado forms between the ascending and descending airflows.

Record Tornado 21st May 1950
The longest lived tornado ever recorded in Britain started around Wendover, Bucks at 4 p.m. and petered out on the Norfolk coast at 8 p.m. During its hundred mile journey over land, the maximum wind speed was estimated to be 230 mph. It was accompanied by large hailstones. Parts of Wendover, Aston Clinton, Puttenham, Linslade, Lidlington, Bedford and Blakeney were devastated.

Record Range 9th May 1973
The greatest range of temperature ever recorded in Britain was at Tummel Bridge, Tayside. From an early morning −7°C the temperature reached an afternoon peak of 22°C in the shade.

Record Heat 1st to 4th May 1990
The hottest start to May ever known in Britain.

JUNE
I was in Britain for the whole summer but it rained on both days.

Waterspout 9th June 1888
Langtoft in Yorkshire is partly destroyed by a waterspout (tornado over the sea). Langtoft was visited by another violent waterspout on 3rd July 1892.

Record Rain 13th to 15th June 1903
The longest period of continuous rain ever recorded in Britain: 58½ hours.

Lightning Strike 14th June 1914
A heavy thunderstorm flooded the District Line on the London Underground, and lightning killed seven people sheltering under a tree on Wandsworth Common.

Storm Invasion 4th June 1944
A storm postponed the Allied landings in France.

Big Hail 8th June 1957
Hailstones at Camelford, Cornwall were seen to bounce one metre up and covered many back yards knee deep in ice.

Record High 29th June 1957
A shade air temperature of 35.5°C in London.

Snow Cricket 2nd June 1975
Snow prevented cricket at Buxton, interrupted play at Colchester and on the same day also fell at Lord's. Snow settled in Edinburgh, Newark, Grantham and Peterborough. In a subsequent dispute with a disbelieving reader, the Press Council ruled that John Arlott had correctly stated in *The Guardian* that snow fell at Lord's.

Warm Swing 6th June 1975
Since 2nd June air temperatures had climbed 20°C – a heatwave began.

Heatwave 25th June 1976
The year of the drought. Temperatures in the shade were greater than 32°C every afternoon somewhere in Britain until 8th July.

Red Rain 29th June 1981
Pink dust fell on cars in Ireland and central Scotland.

Above Hailstones packed together make hard work for the pub helpers at Camelford, Cornwall.

Left Waterspouts can suck up fish from the sea and deposit them miles inland when the parent cloud moves onshore.

JULY
Those dog days of summer.

Hot Tuesday   8th July 1707
Several men and horses died from heat stroke during harvest work in England. Estimated shade air temperature of 38°C.

Late Snow   11th July 1888
Sleet fell in Kent.

Right A section of a giant hailstone. The number of rings within a hailstone tell us the number of orbits the stone has made up into the freezing upper cloud, and down again through the water cloud.

Giant Hail   8th July 1893
Five centimetre diameter hailstones fell on Richmond, Yorkshire.

St Swithin   15th July 1913
There was a fifteen hour downpour on St Swithin's Day in London. Subsequently it rained on only nine out of the following forty days.

Spectacular Storms   10th and 11th July 1923
An all-night display of spectacular lightning over south-east England from a remarkable sequence of thunderstorms.

St Swithin   15th July 1924
On St Swithin's Day there were thirteen and a half hours of blazing sunshine in London. Subsequently it rained on thirty of the following forty days.

Warmest Night   28th July 1948
The warmest ever night-time temperature recorded in Britain was 23.3°C at Westminster.

Record Frost   1st July 1960
An air temperature of -1°C in Norfolk.

Red Rain   1st July 1968
Red rain fell on most of England and Wales. At Guildford large orange blobs covered the town. Liphook, Hants reached 34°C in the shade. Leeming, Yorkshire had nearly four centimetres of rain in eight and a half minutes. Giant hail of eight centimetres in diameter fell on Devon.

Land Devil   30th July 1975
The day was cloudless and the air temperature 22°C at Warmley, Bristol. A land devil, or whirl-wind, picked up a factory and moved it nine metres. The workers watched in amazement as the roof blew off and landed on a car more than a hundred feet away.

Drought Minister   15th July 1976
The first ever Minister of Drought was appointed by the Drought Bill on St Swithin's Day. On 29th August heavy rain fell over the south of England.

Wettest   July 1988
Wettest July since rain records began in 1869, over the north-west.

Best Wine   July 1989
The warmest ever July known in the south of Britain. Thought to be the best wine season since medieval times 800 years ago.

AUGUST
The Great British summer; three fine days and a thunderstorm.

Big Hail   1st August 1846
Hailstones broke 7000 panes of glass in the Houses of Parliament. The glass arcade that covered the pavements of Regent Street was smashed to smithereens.

So Hot   9th August 1911
38°C at Greenwich.

High River   26th August 1912
Twenty centimetres of rain in twelve hours over East Anglia, causing the highest ever flood of the River Wensum through Norwich. All the bridges upstream of the town were swept away; 2500 people were made homeless and 3650 buildings were demolished.

Record Cold   24th August 1940
Air temperature down to −3°C in London. The earliest known frost in London.

Lynmouth Flood   15th August 1952
Twenty-five centimetres of rain in twelve hours from a cloudburst on Exmoor. Massive devastation, 400 people made homeless, 93 homes demolished. 34 people were killed.

Hampstead Storm   14th August 1975
Probably the biggest rainfall on one place in Britain this century. A cloudburst of 17 centimetres of rain fell on Hampstead in three hours. The London Weather Centre just two miles away had only 0.2 inches of rain. Four local rivers, of which most people were probably unaware, rose, burst and sent huge waves over garden walls. Within five minutes of the start of the storm a hundred homes were flooded with several feet of water. One man in a basement was drowned. The sewer manhole covers were forced up, and the Underground was flooded.

Drought Ends   29th August 1976
Downpours ended the worst ever drought for 1000 years over England and Wales. One million people had been forced to use standpipes for eleven weeks. Reservoirs dried out completely and their mud bases cracked.

Daytime Darkness   6th August 1981
Daytime darkness fell on London with a spectacular lightning display.

SEPTEMBER
What dreadful hot weather we have, it keeps one in a continual state of inelegance.

So Hot   September 1906
London reached 35.5°C.

Early Snow   20th September 1919
Earliest known time of year for widespread snow to fall in Britain.

Blue Moon   26th September 1950
A blue moon was seen over Britain. The cause was a forest fire in Alberta, Canada. Drifting smoke with just the right size of particles was able to scatter away the red part of the white reflected sunlight from the moon, while allowing the blue part to pass without interruption. Particles of that size are rarely present in the night sky – just 'once in a blue moon'.

Snow Cover   17th September 1954
The Cairngorms were covered in snow down to 760 metres. During the year of the drought and heatwave of 1976, some snow managed to linger through the usually critical time of September on the Cairngorms.

Record Hail   5th September 1958
The heaviest hailstone ever recorded in Britain fell at Horsham, Sussex at 6 p.m.: six and a half ounces, and about the size of a grapefruit. Small pits were left in lawns where hailstones had fallen. As many as 10,000 bushels of apples were destroyed, and those left on the trees were

Above The terrible Lynmouth flood of August 1952. The river Lyn burst its banks after a huge cloudburst. Houses were torn down and many people drowned.

Old Lady. "WHAT A DREADFUL DOWNPOUR. IT'S A REGULAR WATERSPOUT!"

all hail pitted. There was also an unverified report of a 227 gram hailstone falling at Plumstead in London on 5th July 1925.

Big Flood   15th September 1968
In Guildford the Yvonne Arnaud Theatre was flooded to a depth of one metre, and the Millbrook shopping centre to a depth of two and a half metres.

Tornado   26th September 1971
A tornado moved a ninety ton train 46 metres along its track at Rotherham, Yorkshire.

Hurricane   16th September 1976
Remnants of hurricane Flossie gave gusts up to 104 mph over northern Scotland.

OCTOBER

The season of mists and mellow fruitfulness, and maybe an Indian summer.

Severe Storm   25th October 1859
A severe storm destroyed Brighton pier and sunk the *Royal Charter* off Anglesey. Five hundred people were drowned. This storm led to the setting up of the Meteorological Office. The first gale for which forecast warnings were issued by telegraph was on 1st December 1863 in southern England.

Record Rain   11th October 1916
Heaviest known rainfall in a day in Scotland. Twenty centimetres fell at Loch Hourn.

Old Wives' Summer   6th October 1921
Latest known date for shade air temperatures more than 29°C in London. An old wives' summer is a period of fine weather that begins sometime between the middle of September and first week of October.

Long Drought   10th October 1959
A drought of fifty-nine days over eastern England ends.

Hurricane   16th October 1987
The second most destructive storm ever to hit southern Britain. It devastated the south-east of England in the small hours. Eighteen people lost their lives as a direct result.

NOVEMBER

No warmth, no cheerfulness, no heathful ease, No comfortable feel in any member No shade, no shine, no butterflies, no bees, No fruits, no flowers, no leaves, no birds, – November!

Record Rain   11th November 1929
Largest known one day rainfall in Wales: Twenty-one centimetres at Lluest reservoir.

Thick Smog   19th November 1936
The most prolonged fog since records began in Manchester and Birmingham. On 26th November very acid rain fell out of the fog (pH 3). On 28th November all that could be seen in the streets was the kerb. Metals changed colour, aircraft icing was black, and everything was covered in black wet slime.

So Hot   5th November 1938
Warmest November day ever known in London: 21°C.

Below Just some of the devastation caused by the hurricane of October 1987.

So Hot   4th November 1946

Warmest November day ever recorded in Britain: 22°C at Prestatyn, north Wales.

Thick Smog   22nd November 1948

The start of a ten day smog (smoke plus fog) in central and eastern England.

Bizarre   1st November 1965

Three giant power station cooling towers at Ferrybridge, Yorkshire collapsed in air turbulence.

Red Rain   28th November 1979

An estimated 60,000 tonnes of dust from the Sahara fell on the Cork region. Gritty sandy rain fell on Blackpool. Red rain fell on Dublin. Pink dust covered cars in Scotland and Northern Ireland.

DECEMBER

And the snow lay round about, deep and crisp and even.

Christmas Storm   25th December 1836

The heaviest Christmas Day snowstorm ever recorded in Britain, with drifts twenty feet deep. Virtually all roads were impassable across England. Many people died.

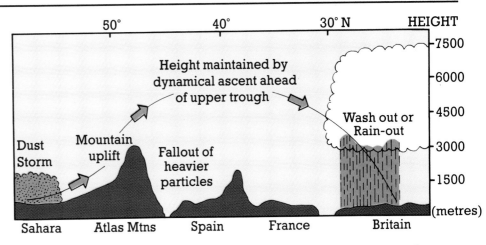

A schematic diagram of possible dust transport from the Sahara to the British Isles.

Avalanche   27th December 1836

The only snow avalanche ever to have happened in Britain was at Lewes, Sussex. An overhang of snow from the Cliffe Hills broke away in the sunshine and demolished two houses. Eight people were killed.

Unofficial   4th December 1879

Unofficially the coldest night ever in Britain: −30°C at Blackadder, Berwickshire. Reports of many people frozen to death.

Pea-Souper   5th December 1962

The worst pea-souper ever known in London and the Thames valley lasted four days. Soot and sulphur in the fog made acid smog; this

Left The strange effects of skyscrapers floating above the thick smog below.

Left King's Lynn, 1981. Mini-iceburgs from the North Sea in the Wash at King's Lynn, Norfolk.

combined with temperatures below freezing resulted in the death of 4000. People died of bronchitis and pneumonia. The weight of soot in the air increased from the usual 0.5 to 4.5 milligrams per cubic metre.

White Christmas   25th December 1970
This was the last true white Christmas, with snow falling in London and the south-east. That year many parts of Britain had snow lying for the twelve days of Christmas. Previous white Christmases in London were 1906, 1927 and 1938, and just about making it were 1917, 1923 and 1956. The year 1981 very nearly made it as a white Christmas. It was a very snowy December that year from London northwards, but no snow fell on Christmas Day in London. It turned out to be the coldest December on record: eleven December days in 1981 had temperatures below −10°C. Since 1931 the earliest snow fall recorded in London was on 8th December. The heavy Boxing Day snowfall across many parts of the country started the most severe winter since 1740.

Tornado   1st December 1975
Seven tornadoes over East Anglia.

Sea Ice   15th December 1981
The most recent sea ice along the east coast of England.

It's worth noting that our present calendar has seasons as follows:

Winter: December, January, February
Spring: March, April, May
Summer: June, July, August
Autumn: September, October, November

Weatherwise it would be better to adjust the seasons like this:

Winter: mid November to mid February
Spring: mid February to mid May
Summer: mid May to mid August
Autumn: mid August to mid November

Another interesting fact is that 1989 was the warmest year since temperature records began in 1659. Could this mean something?

WEATHER AND HEALTH

Mad dogs and Englishmen go out in the midday sun.

Noel Coward, *Words and Music*

Gradual transformation scene. –
Flight of the demon influenza at the approach of spring.

The great British obsession with weather is due to the fact that weather affects our comfort, our well-being, our physical health and our mental state.

The change of mood that weather can bring is in itself quite amazing. For instance imagine, after days and days of dull dank dreary weather, a sudden change to brilliant sunshine. How that weather change lifts the spirits, and how much more cheerful everyone seems. Remember the first sunny days of spring after the gloom of winter – what a tonic, what vitality the weather change adds to life. Everyone can remember that feeling. It is a time when people are full of the joys of spring, a time when 'a young man's fancy lightly turns to thoughts of love'.

The more dramatic the weather change, the more intense the change of mood. A polar front is a fairly dramatic weather feature, bringing a change to brisk crisp bright weather. Thunderstorms can have this effect too. Polar fronts and thunderstorms are more common in the USA, and can stimulate great enthusiasm for life. No wonder Americans seem so vigorous and so intense about things. I suspect that what the Americans die from in the end is enthusiasm, whereas British folk, well, they probably die of patience.

The different climates around the world rub off on the people that live in them, causing identifiable national character traits. Compare the zest of the American with the reserve of the

"In the Spring a young man's fancy – –"

Right How a change in the weather can make a change in your mood. This stimulating and invigorating scene could easily lift the spirits or fill one with awe.

English. Compare the explosive temper of the Italian with the calm mild nature of the man from Tipperary, where 'time stands still'. Then there is the tenacious no-nonsense Scottish Highlander. It is my feeling (being Scottish myself) that the reason so many Scotsmen are successful is that hard work is drummed into them at an early age. For as long as anyone can remember it has been necessary to work hard in order to live in the hostile, wild and windy Highlands of Scotland.

> 'Tis hard grey weather
> Breeds hard English men.
>
> Charles Kingsley,
> *Ode to the North-East Wind*

The science that examines the influence of weather on living things is called biometeorology. Just as when psychiatry first started it had its critics, so it is with biometeorology.

After all, how can the effect of weather on health be measured? Certainly some people seem to know they are weather sensitive. Bunions and corns are the archetypal weather forecasting tools.

An instrument called an algimeter tests for weather sensitive aches and pains. The instrument slowly applies more and more stimulus to the person until a change in blood pressure shows the person feels pain. Researchers have found that much less stimulus is needed to cause pain during changeable weather than during settled spells. So people are sensitive to weather changes – yet few of us are aware of it. Usually the effect is small, but for vulnerable people like the elderly, the very young or the ill, weather effects are important.

This is why doctors will sometimes recommend particular weather regions for convalescence, and different regions for different illnesses. A relaxing climate produces a

Above Unpolluted crisp polar air often invades Scotland, producing vast and magnificent skies.

Below The way we all feel when it's very cold!

sedative effect. This type of climate is typically rather cloudy, humid and mild with just a small range of temperature between day and night. It is usually beneficial to those recovering from the strain of overwork. On the other hand a bracing climate is stimulating and tones up the body. This climate is typically rather cool and fresh with plenty of sunshine and a wide range of temperature between day and night. It is usually of benefit to those recovering from operations.

During the 1600s and through Victorian times, sick people had precious little to help them. It was recognised that water was a natural healer, and in particular mineral springs, alleged to be the source of magical cures since medieval times. They were something that ill people could turn to. Mineral water resorts, or spa towns, sprang up to cash in on rich people trying to heal themselves by taking the cure, living by the spa and drinking the water.

In 1620 Mrs Elizabeth Farrow of Scarborough discovered the first of two mineral springs on Scarborough's beach. She noticed how the iron in the water turned the pebbles brown. Such was the power of taking the waters that, despite the northern location, Scarborough became a thriving spa town. In fact by 1730 Scarborough was Britain's first seaside resort. Sea bathing apparently helped in drying up 'superfluous humours', keeping them from rotting, while also 'killing all manner of worms'. The mineral water cure was recommended by doctors for all sorts of ailments, ranging from 'windiness' to 'leprosie'.

However, many doctors suspected that the real benefit from a spa visit or seaside resort visit was as much to do with the change of

Above Taking the waters at Scarborough in 1884.

Left Scarborough from the Spa, 1850 by H. B. Carter. In the 17th century, Scarborough was a popular spa and by the 1730s it had become Britain's first seaside resort.

climate as anything else. Consequently a great British obsession developed: climotherapy. From the 1700s onwards it was fashionable for eminent doctors to prescribe climotherapy – the treatment of disease by going to a beneficial climate. Bognor Regis is indeed famous for being favoured by King George II and his son. The story goes that on his death-bed in London, when given the news that the sun was coming out again in Bognor, his last words were 'bugger Bognor'. Brighton, Weymouth and Southampton were also patronised by royalty concerned for their state of health. Mineral waters, sea air, sunshine, fine scenery, assembly rooms, promenades and pleasure gardens became recognised as almost synonymous with healing climates.

Climate guides for the sick and afflicted were published at seaside resorts. For example, William Harwood somehow managed to distinguish five separate climates at Hastings. People with wasting diseases, he wrote, needed

The Royal Victoria Spa & Assembly Rooms, Southampton

Above The Spa and Assembly Rooms, Southampton — where the fashionable went to 'see and be seen'. The spa water was so popular that it was even bottled and exported to the East and West Indies.

Left The popular resort of Bognor Regis. Although bathing and sea air were thought to be beneficial, 'modesty must prevail' at all times for the Victorians, with the aid of 'Bathing Machines'.

warmth, stable temperature and no wind. There-fore they should not stay in the upper parts of the town where it was two or three hundred feet above sea level, as it was a coat colder. Harwood listed streets which were good for lung patients during certain seasons, and streets that were good for asthmatics during others. Apparently, Hastings High Street was of benefit to lung patients in winter, but harmful to tuberculosis patients at that time. Remarkably, a chosen street could be of benefit against one disease up to a certain house number, and then no more as the incidence of colder winds took over.

Torquay was mapped to show which hotels received the most sun and wind. One eminent physician observed at the time that Frying-pan Walk in Torquay was 'filled in general with respiratory bearing people who look like puzzled ghosts and are ugly enough to frighten young people to death'. Torquay was attracting many elderly people who suffered from tuber-culosis of the lung. Further down the coast, claimed another climate guide, Dawlish 'greets the pulmonary patient in December, and the nervous melancholy makes it his home in the merry month of May'.

In spring, Chelsea and Kensington were fine for bronchial patients. Alternatively, people with breathing problems might try Eastbourne or St Leonards-on-Sea where the air, claimed the climate guides, 'is exception-ally pure and free from infectious diseases'. Ilfracombe could boast in its climate guide that a significant number of its residents lived to be one hundred years of age. Margate was recommended for those with slow healing body wounds. Aberystwyth in sheltered Cardigan Bay was best for people suffering from overwork. Further north on the Yorkshire coast near Redcar, Saltburn-by-the-Sea was just the job for listless, flagging and spiritless people in need of revival.

Penzance, with its exceptionally mild climate all year long, could claim to be the Montpellier of the far south coast. Montpellier was the magic name in climotherapy. This French Riviera town, with plenty of sunshine and very little rain, was of great benefit to those with catarrhal diseases; however, the wind was a little too sharp for most lung patients. Ironically almost every British spa town claimed to be the Montpellier of its region, even naming roads 'Montpellier Avenue' and houses 'Montpellier Villas' for good measure.

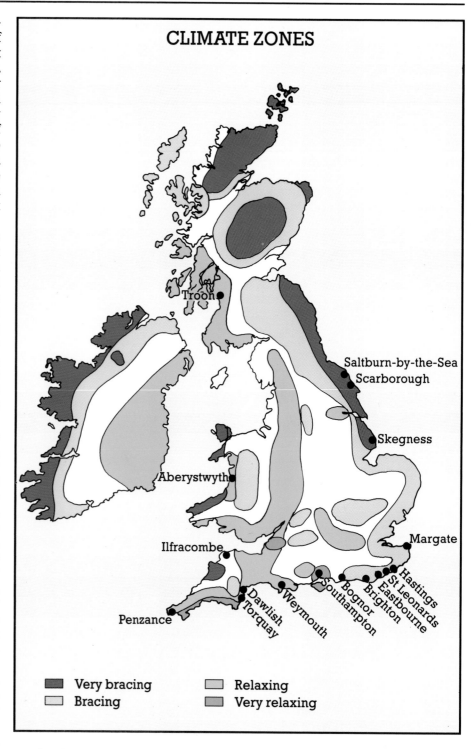

CLIMATE ZONES

Very bracing
Bracing
Relaxing
Very relaxing

During the 1800s lung patients seeking a cure began to change direction. Medical reports from England and Germany identified dry frosty air and exercise as beneficial. Doctors began to prescribe stays in cold mountain climates, even in winter. The age of the sana-torium began.

Above Early resort towns were mostly in the south of England. On any one day it is possible for the weather to be totally different from the climate zones.

During Victorian times, the scientist, Louis Pasteur made new discoveries in bacteria; this diverted attention away from climotherapy to the study of antibiotics. Interest in climate cures was renewed when Niels Minsen demonstrated that sunlight therapy could treat tuberculosis of the skin. He was awarded the Nobel prize in 1903. Sanatoriums were set up in England and especially in the Swiss Alps to treat tubercular patients. Nowadays the sanatoriums are used for convalescence, since sunlight helps protect patients from infective organisms.

While some types of weather will ameliorate illnesses, other weathers will aggravate them:

- Hypothermia, hyperthermia and skin cancer are directly linked to weather.

- Bronchitis, rheumatism, asthma and hay fever are illnesses that may be exacerbated by the weather.

- Plague, poliomyelitis and malaria are caused by germs that will spread large distances if the weather permits.

- Heart attack, stroke and the common cold are existing conditions that may be triggered by certain weathers.

- Crimes of passion, riot, depression, suicide and epileptic fits are states of mental imbalance that may also be triggered by certain weather conditions.

It should be understood that weather does not cause disease and illness, but may be a contributory factor.

Hypothermia is a deep core body temperature below the normal 37°C, which raises the blood pressure and increases the clotting factor in the blood of vulnerable people. The amount of heat people generate decreases with age. The elderly cannot shiver up body heat as well as they used to. They are more sedentary, therefore generating less heat, are less sensitive to changes in temperature.

However, during cold wintry weather the great majority of patients who are admitted to hospital with hypothermia have some serious underlying illness that has been responsible for the hypothermia, not the other way round. One study, after the cold spell of 1986, showed that the death rate was identical for old people in warm sheltered housing as for everyone else. It seems that although people keep warm at home during the day, they tend to open windows and

Deep body temperature °C	AVERAGE REACTION TO THERMAL STRESS
42	death
41	heat stroke, unconscious, hypothalamus ceases to function
40	heat exhaustion, collapse
39	irritable, flushed, prickly heat
38	heavy sweating
37	NORMAL
36	shivering
35	disorientation
34	loss of memory
33	collapse
32	loss of reflexes, hypothalamus ceases to function
31	heart unable to contract enough
30	death normally follows

Below Either they are thick-skinned, or they drink a particular brand of lager!

Above Hoods keep in the cocoon of warm air that is lost through the head. Pulling faces helps ward off frostbite — and probably friends too!

which then loses less heat. However, the constriction process causes the blood pressure to rise. This can trigger illness in someone with circulation problems. The real danger in cold turn off heating during the night. The great British obsession with fresh air may be just as important as poor heating in causing excess deaths during cold spells. Another danger for elderly people during the winter is having to wait at bus stops for long periods, allowing the cold to affect their circulation system.

As the body temperature falls the mind wanders strangely. Motorcycle riders on long cold journeys can drop body temperature by 2°C, and experience a sense of detachment, typical of exposure victims. In a confused mental state, hypothermia sufferers have been known to remove their clothes – a phenomenon called 'paradoxical undressing' or 'mountain disrobing syndrome'.

The most important weather element affecting the human body is heat (or lack of it). Man is like an automatic heating and cooling system designed to run at 37°C. Our origins are the tropics of East Africa. Thinking man discovered fire, and made shelters and clothes to overcome the weather elements that nature had not endowed him to endure. Nowadays people live in virtually all parts of the world, but still a cold climate is harder to cope with than a warm climate, even though the body can easily contend with the cold by simply wrapping up in more clothes.

On cold days the first reaction of the body is to begin to close up the surface blood vessels so that less blood reaches the body surface,

WINDCHILL TABLE

Air temp °C	5	10	15	20	25	30	
+5	+4	0	3	5	6	8	8
+4	+3	1	4	6	7	10	10
+3	+2	2	6	7	9	11	11
+2	+1	3	7	9	10	12	13
+1	0	4	9	10	12	14	15
0	1	5	10	12	13	15	16
1	2	6	11	13	14	16	17
2	3	7	12	15	16	18	19
3	4	8	14	16	17	19	20
4	5	9	15	17	19	21	22
5	6	10	16	19	20	22	23
6	7	11	17	20	21	24	25
7	8	12	19	22	23	25	26
8	9	14	20	23	24	27	28
9	10	15	22	24	26	28	29
10	11	16	23	26	27	30	31
11	12	17	24	27	28	31	32
12	13	18	25	29	30	33	34
13	14	20	27	30	31	34	35
14	15	21	28	31	33	36	37
15	16	22	29	33	34	37	38
16	17	23	30	34	35	38	40
17	18	24	32	36	37	40	41
18	19	26	33	37	38	41	43
19	20	27	35	38	40	43	45
20	21	28	36	40	41	44	46

Windchill equivalent temperatures can be read for the days temperature and wind.
All numbers are minus °C (except +'s).

☐ Bitter   ■ Frostbite

weather is the wind. Strong winds have an enormous cooling power.

On a still, clear day with a temperature of 20°C and 50 per cent humidity, the average person radiates about 250 watts from bare skin. Skin has an insulating cocoon of warm air a few millimetres thick at the feet, increasing to several centimetres above the head. The cocoon of warm air quite naturally rises into the cooler air of the environment, but this convection normally proceeds at a very slow rate. The cooling power of the wind – windchill – comes from speeding up the convection rate. The faster the wind, the greater the heat loss. When the heat loss cannot be replaced by the body's metabolic process or sun heat, then life can be threatened.

On the face of it this windchill might seem a bit of a fudge, contrived to exaggerate the degree of cold. A way of proving the existence of windchill is to put two bowls of water outside on a windy night with an air temperature below 0°C. One bowl should be exposed to the wind, the other behind a windbreak. You will notice that the water in the exposed bowl freezes first because of the cooling power of the wind. It should be remembered that the mixture of water and antifreeze in your car, just like the water in the bowls, cannot be cooled *below* the air temperature no matter how hard the wind blows, so extra antifreeze is not needed as some garage mechanics would have you believe.

Exposed water pipes around the house will freeze quicker if the wind can reach them. If the ice cannot expand freely the pipes will burst. When the thaws come, so must the plumber.

If wrapping up against the cold it is important to let the skin breathe. Excessive clothing causes the body to sweat. The sweat in turn breaks down the insulating qualities of the clothing and draws heat from the body. Water cools the body about thirty times faster than still air of the same temperature. In tropical waters at 18°C, three hours in the water is often fatal. In North Sea waters in winter at 6°C, three minutes in the water can also be fatal.

In accounting for the distribution of heart disease across Britain, frequent changes in exposure to cold stress, through climate or poor housing, may be a significant factor. The rates of heart disease match regional variations in stress produced by cold. As you go further north and west so the weather changes more frequently and gets that much colder. It is known, for example, that manual workers in East Anglia with poorer housing have a lower heart disease rate than professional people in the north and north-west.

The effects of hot weather on health can be just as dangerous as cold. In particular it is the combination of hot days, high humidity and no wind that causes extreme problems. The body responds to heat stress by a dramatic increase in heartbeat rate (heart strain). Blood vessels dilate so that up to seven times the amount of blood can flow through the skin vessels. This flushing releases heat to the outside air. However, when the air temperature exceeds the skin temperature, heat control depends solely on the evaporation of sweat.

"Bring me two eggs."   "On toast, Sir?"   "No—on ice."

Man has some two million sweat glands, capable of secreting ten litres in a day. Man sweats more than any other animal, even the pig (which only sweats on its snout). Evaporating just one litre of sweat takes 650 watts from the body – cooling it enormously. It is precisely because the body loses large amounts of heat by evaporation that people can tolerate dry heat more than damp or humid heat. If the air is saturated with water vapour (100 per cent humidity), sweat cannot evaporate into the air and so the body overheats.

Overheating causes heat exhaustion when the blood flow system fails to compensate for the dilation of the blood vessels. The nervous system is starved of its usual supply of blood,

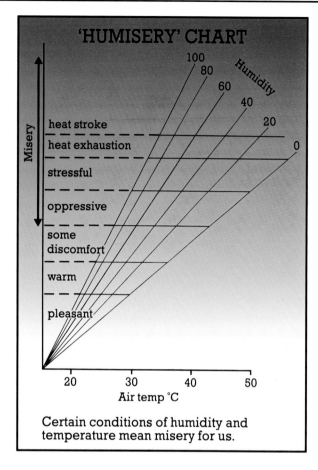

'HUMISERY' CHART

Certain conditions of humidity and
temperature mean misery for us.

common. There are perhaps a dozen a year in
England and Wales, maybe a few in Scotland
and Ireland, and none on the coasts. In fact the
coast is the best place to be during hot weather,
as you have the sea-breeze by day and the land
breeze by night.

In the extreme, it is just possible that the
riots in 1981 at Brixton, Toxteth, Southall, St Pauls
and Handsworth were exacerbated by the
exceptionally warm humid weather that affected
all the people involved simultaneously. People
rioting are very hot, therefore increasing their
metabolic rate. If the air adds to that stress by
being oppressively sultry then spiralling
emotions can lead to highly irrational thoughts.
Weather of course does not cause riots, and
perhaps the only link is that more people will be
out on the street on a warm summer night.

Lazing by the sea on a warm, sunny day
certainly feels much nicer than scurrying

Right The 1981 riots in
Brixton, south London. The
hot, humid weather during
this period could have been
a contributory factor to the
unrest.

causing headache, dizziness and fatigue, leading to collapse. Statistics are hard to find on heat
exhaustion, but for example many field workers
have died during hot harvest weather from heat
stroke. The death toll from heat stroke among
the elderly rose by more than 50 per cent during the weeks of June and July 1976, the year of
the heatwave.

Overweight people and people with a heart
condition are most stressed by the hot weather.
Hot weather can also affect mental balance.
People tend to be more irritable on sultry days
and tempers can flare. Of course in Britain hot
sultry days are few and far between, although
this may change as we slip into the more Mediterranean climate induced by the greenhouse
effect. Oppressively hot weather abroad is
sometimes taken into account in courts dealing
with crimes of passion, riots, murders and
suicides. The hot wind from Africa crosses the
Mediterranean to reach the European coast as a
moist sultry oppressive wind called the sirocco.
This wind is often associated with low gloomy
stratus and sticky nights when even the furniture
is dripping. Luckily in Britain sultry days are not

around in business clothes during hot weather. Today suntans are fashionable, perhaps even status symbols too. Heliophobia (fear of the sun) is quite rare nowadays, but it was not so long ago – within the living memory of some people – that the sun was regarded as an enemy to be warded off. The parasol warded off the ray, not the rain. Linen sun-hats warded off the dreaded sunstroke. Net curtains warded off the sun from furniture and fabrics. Some people even closed blinds on Sunday to shut the demon sun out of the holy day. The umbrella was something to ward off the sun; the word comes from the Latin *umbra*, meaning a shadow. Throughout history writers have tended to cast the sun – the blazing sun – as a persecutor, probably because much of literature derives from Greek teachings where the high summer can be exhaustingly oppressive. Hence the desire to be in a 'shady nook by a babbling brook'.

In Britain the most dangerous time to be exposed to sunshine is late June around the middle part of the day when the skies are a clear deep blue, and above the bright sandy beach brilliant cumulus litter the half of the sky away from the sun. On such a day there is maximum penetration of ultraviolet sunlight through a minimum depth of uncontaminated atmosphere, plus maximum indirect ultraviolet sunlight reflected from cloud and sand.

Doctors in Australia have suggested that 50,000 hours or more exposure to sunshine will probably bring on some form of skin cancer in most white people. In Britain, Cornwall has the highest rate of skin cancer. This is due to its southerly latitude, enabling Cornish folk to clock up more sunshine hours and thereby soak up more ultraviolet (UV), the high energy sunshine wavelengths with the most number of waves per second hitting the skin. This UV radi-

Below Sun worshippers flock in their hundreds to bathe under the sun's precious rays.

Right As well as direct sunshine, there is sunshine reflected from the sea, the sand and from the white clouds.

ation from the sun can be divided into three distinct biologically active wavelength ranges:

- **UVA** activates melanin in the skin, causing tanning.

- **UVB** does the same, but being more energetic can cause sunburn among fair-skinned people which can lead to skin cancer.

- **UVC** is stopped from reaching people by the ozone shield high in the atmosphere, which is just as well because that high energy radiation causes mutations and skin cancer by killing DNA molecules.

Skin cancer is normally curable, and there are about 20,000 new cases each year. Melanoma is the only skin cancer that spreads to distant parts of the body, and consequently the death rate from melanoma is high; there are typically a few hundred new cases each year in Britain. Malignant melanoma is most common among fair-skinned people who burn easily. In melanoma cases it is not the hours clocked up in the sun but rather the sudden exposure to high intensity UV that does the damage. Those without natural protection (a tan) from UV should be wary of overdosing in hotter countries.

SKIN TYPES		
Celtic	freckles red hair	burn easily no tan
Northern	freckles blue/hazel eyes red/blonde hair	tan slightly
Most white people	fair skin	tan slowly
Mediterranean Chinese Japanese	olive skin	tan easily
Indian Arab	brown skin	tan deeply
Negroes	brown/black	never burn

There are of course great benefits to be had from sunshine. Sunshine produces vitamin D, which is important because it maintains the correct level of calcium and magnesium in the body. A deficiency of calcium and magnesium can lead to mental and neurological disorders like hyperventilation (lack of oxygen to the brain), depression, anxiety, insomnia and general tension. Sunbathing, or irradiation of the blood through the skin, can increase the oxygen-carrying capacity of the blood, lower the blood cholesterol level and lower the blood pressure. So sunbathing has a soothing and relaxing effect on everyone, bringing welcome relief from stress. Of course many people need stimulation, and so cannot take much sunbathing without becoming uncomfortably bored, but it does seem that 'a little of what you fancy does you good'.

Sunlight, by triggering the natural production of vitamin D, acts as a major deterrent to breast and colon cancer. A study in Russia and the USA found there was a threefold increase in the incidence of breast cancer in low sunlight areas. Diet is also a crucial variable. Japan, on the same latitudes as the USA, has a low incidence of breast cancer owing to the Japanese habit of eating enormous amounts of fish, which is rich in vitamin D. The link between cancer and lack of vitamin D roughly parallels that of rickets and vitamin D deficiency, which was a big problem in nineteenth-century industrial towns across Britain. In 1919 it was shown that sunlight could cure rickets. The National Health Service finally put a stop to rickets in children by supplying free cod liver oil rich in vitamin D.

.I.HAVE. NOT.SEEN. THE.SUN. FOR.FOURTEEN. WEEKS.

Lack of sunshine in January and February causes half a million people (mostly women) in Britain to suffer a form of winter depression known as seasonally affective disorder (SAD). This clinical depression, unlike other sorts of depression, has been proved to be due to lack of sunshine. This is because exposure in full spectrum (2000 lux) light boxes, for between ten and sixty minutes a day, actually lifts the depression within about a week. For three out of four people, provided the dosage is kept up, the depression is kept at bay. These people are clearly sensitive to the solar cycle, but to a lesser degree. Some people, no doubt, suffer damaging mental symptoms in the low light months, but somehow manage to shrug it off. Perhaps that rare dazzlingly sunny winter day can induce an emotional happy feeling of well-being.

One of the most important findings in twenty years' study of the biology of depression is that hospital admissions with mania are a lot more common in winter than summer months. A much higher proportion of people suffer mood disorders in December, January and February.

In the summer months the warm weather and sunshine bring on the hay fever season. Hay fever is a curious name for it, since it has nothing to do with hay, nor does it cause a fever. Seasonal allergic rhinitis, to give it its medical title, causes a lot of sneezing, an itchy, blocked or runny nose, itchy eyes which may also be red, watery and sensitive to light, and an itchy throat. One in ten people in Britain suffers symptoms during the months of June, July and August. The season is usually at its height around the end of June and the beginning of July.

LITERAL.

"Ullo, Brown, how are you?"—"Very well, thanks."
"How are you at Home?"—"My Wife says I'm very Grumpy."

A measure of the severity of the season is the pollen count, which can reach 200 grains of grass pollen per cubic metre of air breathed in urban areas. A count of fifty will usually cause those affected to suffer some symptoms. A count of more than 100 is high. The pollen count published in newspapers is, unfortunately, virtually useless because it is so out of date. The pollen grains are collected over twenty-four hours, then counted under a microscope, then released to the media, then put into the next edition. All this takes time, so the pollen count is really the pollen count of one or two days ago at the particular site of the pollen collector. The source of pollen count for the national press has been on the roof at St Mary's Hospital, Paddington, London for over twenty years now. Just how representative is such a site is arguable, but clearly London cannot represent anywhere else, especially the north of England and Scotland where the season starts around late June.

A forecast pollen count for the day ahead is now made by the weather centres around the country, because as well as the time of year the count depends mostly on the weather. For example, a day of heavy rain will wash the pollen grains down to the ground and the count will be low. At the other extreme, a cloud-free June or July morning with a light breeze from the grasslands and a marked low altitude temperature inversion (the kind of day when chimney smoke travels horizontally) has the potential for a very high count. However, typically the bright early morning sun triggers the release of grass pollen. Thermals rise into the light winds and carry the pollen aloft and onward, usually until about tea-time, when the thermals lose their buoyancy so that the pollen grains filter down to nose level again. The peak pollen count time is often around the end of the afternoon. However, since each day's weather is different, the precise nature of the pollen count will vary from day to day. For example, a wind off the sea (the coast is a good place to live to avoid hay fever) will have virtually no pollen grains, whereas a long land track wind over grasslands will have many.

Pollen, which is too small to see, enters the body through the nose and mouth, and in an

Above A bee orchid.
Right a grassy meadow. Some people are sensitive to tree and flower pollen, but most hay fever sufferers are allergic to grass pollen released into the wind in high summer.

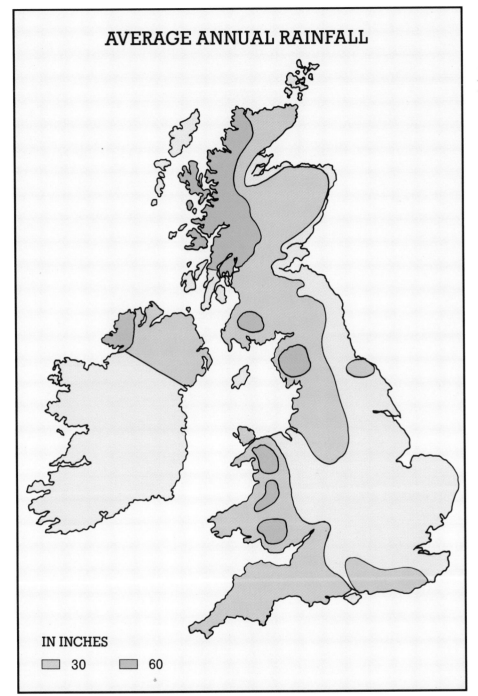

AVERAGE ANNUAL RAINFALL

IN INCHES

30   60

RAIN-BASKING: THE NEW ENGLISH PASTIME

THE IMPERVIOUS PATRIOT. "Ah, Toby, my boy, they've got nothing like this on the Lido."

Left The wettest parts of Britain are the north and west. These places are the worst areas for bronchitis sufferers if there is also a high incidence of air pollution, fogs and smogs.

allergic person the body's defence system reacts to the pollen as if it were a poison, releasing antibodies. The antibodies interact with the pollen, leading to the release of histamine which causes the hay fever. So, on a forecast high count day, it is possible to take antihistamine drugs to suppress the symptoms. The snag is, though, that the forecast count is only as accurate as the forecast weather – and that's another story! However, as the hay fever season advances the symptoms recorded in 'sneezing diaries' show an increasing lag effect, so that the published pollen count becomes more useful as a guide for hay fever sufferers.

More common than heatwaves or big freeze-ups are long spells of damp wet weather. Although not true, most foreigners imagine it is always raining in Britain.

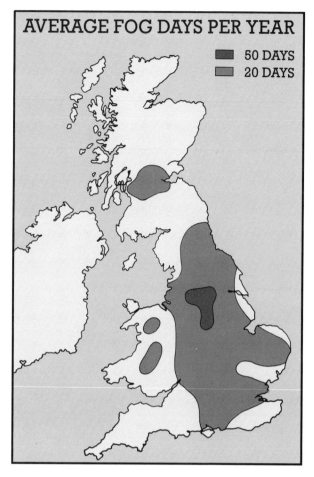

AVERAGE FOG DAYS PER YEAR

■ 50 DAYS
▨ 20 DAYS

In some countries bronchitis is known as the British disease, because until recently Britain was the world leader for deaths from bronchitis – undoubtedly due to all that wet weather! Certainly in Scandinavian countries where the air is clean and fresh the death rate from bronchitis is tiny, whereas in Britain tens of thousands of people die from bronchitis every year. On the 5th December 1952 a thick pool of fog formed in London and the Thames valley. Smoke from coal fires turned the fog into smog that clung on for four days. Deaths from bronchitis increased sevenfold. Although the weather does not cause the disease, damp, fog and pollution will provoke bronchitis. The national pattern for bronchitis is linked to weather, modified by important factors such as cold damp housing, smoking and local factory pollution.

Arthritis and rheumatism can be made worse by cold wet weather. These medical terms are used to cover a wide range of the aches and pains that people complain of, from a passing stiffness in the joints to a serious inflammation of diseased joints. Many sufferers who keep a diary of the weather at times of pain in their joints point to low air pressure, damp and cold during changeable spells of weather as the worse periods. Contrary to the popular belief that arthritis in Britain is worse in winter, the

Right Londoners nicknamed their smogs 'pea-soupers', presumably because the smog was as thick as pea-soup. Since the Clean Air Act of 1956, 'pea-soupers' have become extinct.

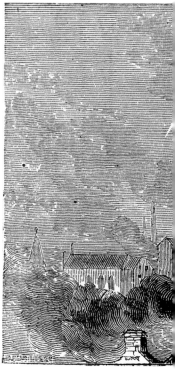

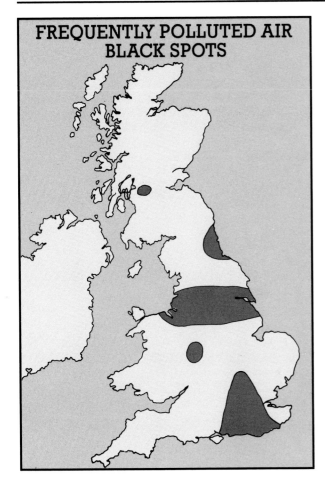

FREQUENTLY POLLUTED AIR
BLACK SPOTS

greatest number of consultations with GPs take place in spring, the time of changeable weather.

Changing air pressure between the skin and internal body tissues requires fluids to move and tissues to stretch or relax. Falling air pressure and rising humidity as rain approaches lower the partial pressure of oxygen in the air. This could lead to a lowered blood oxygen content in some people. Changing temperature causes the blood flow rate to change as capillaries constrict and then dilate. Someone with arthritis might well find that all these changes brought about by the weather do

Above Smoke plus fog (smog) is trapped below a lid of clear air. The smog cannot rise into the warmer air above. Smoke will rise a little and spread out horizontally below the inversion.

Left This industrial scene of Manchester in the mid 1800s shows the terrible living conditions caused by the hundreds of factories polluting the air.

cause additional pain to damaged inflamed joints. However, the aches and pains we all feel from time to time should not be blamed on the weather.

It would be convenient if we could blame our bad behaviour on a turn in the weather. Föhn sickness can affect some people who live near the Welsh mountains, the Pennines, or the Highlands of Scotland. Föhns are hot dry gusty winds that blow down the mountain sides. The prevailing wind hits the mountain range, but cannot go through the mountains. The forced ascent cools the air to condensation so that its moisture is left on the windward side, and so the wind feels exceptionally dry and warm. Published reports indicate that some people cannot concentrate properly when the föhn is strong, and there is an increase of accidents, crimes and strange behaviour. In Israel, where the hot wind is called the sharav, researchers into föhn sickness have suggested an excess of positive ions in the wind as the cause of changed behaviour. It is like having a lot of static in the air. Some people claim that a negative ioniser in the home creates a healthier atmosphere.

It may well be that some people's nervous systems are sensitive to the changing electrical state of the atmosphere. Electrical storm phobias cause some people to lock themselves away, or even spend the entire day sitting on an underground tube train.

The weather in Britain, seemingly benign, may cut deeper than we think.

Left It is easy to imagine warm gusting winds racing down these slopes.

A HISTORY OF THE BRITISH STORM

Poor naked wretches, wheresoe'er
you are, that bide the pelting of this
pitiless storm.

William Shakespeare, *King Lear*

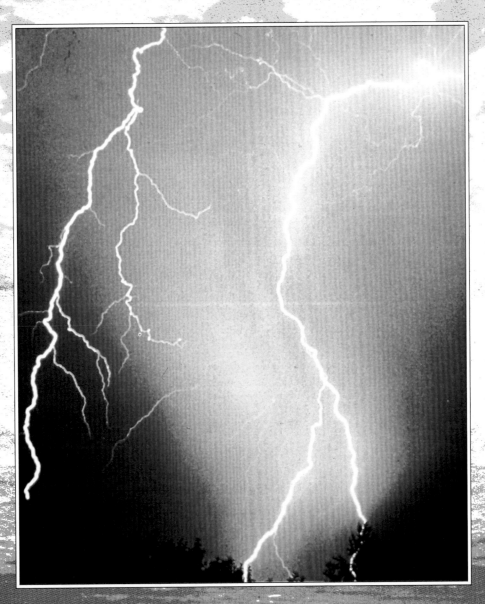

Historically, since the 1500s, two dozen or so severe storms have been recorded over Britain:

1570–1720	twelve major storms
1703, December	Defoe storm, 8,000 killed
1839, January	Menai suspension bridge damaged
1879, December	Tay bridge blown away
1884, January	lowest ever pressure in Britain (926 mbar)
1952, January	Orkneys devastated
1953, February	East Anglian coasts flooded
1962, February	Sheffield devastated by wave wind off Pennines
1968, January	Glasgow 'hurricane'
1973, April	East Midlands devastated
1976, January	Northern Ireland, Lancashire, Midlands, East Anglia devastated
1979, August	Fastnet storm savages yacht race
1987, October	'hurricane' takes everyone by surprise
1990, January	six storms devastate northern Europe in January and February

The storms of 1703, 1987 and 1990 were major events with wind speeds in excess of hurricane force, 73 mph.

7th–8th December 1703

The greatest storm ever to hit Britain was the tempest of 7th–8th December 1703. Observations from ten places in Britain and the nearby Continent indicate that the wind probably peaked at 170 mph over the North Sea. Daniel Defoe (author of *Robinson Crusoe*) advertised for reports about the storm and collated all the information he could, discarding anything that seemed exaggerated. One woman told how she opened her door to get out of the collapsing house, thought better of it, but could not shut the door against the wind, which then blew all night straight through her house. One man in Oxfordshire told how 'a spout marching with the wind like the trunk of an elephant, snapped the body of an oak, sucked up water from cart ruts, tumbled an old barn and twisted its thatch in the air.' Tornadoes were twisting and lifting whole wheatstacks and throwing them down intact in other fields. At Whitstable, Kent, a ship at sea was lifted right out of the water and tossed hundreds of metres inland. A town in Norfolk was almost burnt to the ground, because on the windward side no one could get close enough to the first fire for fear of being blown into it, whereas on the sheltered side it was also impossible because of the intense heat.

Right A guesstimated surface isobaric chart of the tempest in 1703. The track of the storm centre is west to east, with winds spiralling around the centre. It is like an out of control merry-go-round on the back of a slow moving lorry.

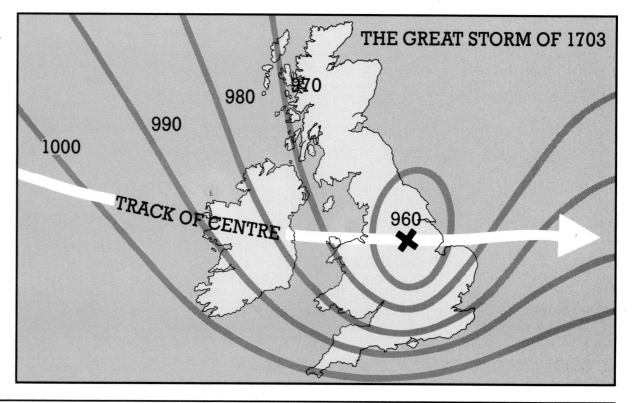

THE GREAT STORM OF 1703

1000 990 980 970 960

TRACK OF CENTRE

Left The author, Daniel Defoe was inspired by the great storm of 1703 to write the book *Robinson Crusoe*.

South of Liverpool across to the Humber, Wales and England were completely devastated. The hurricane force gusts caused serious structural damage. Cathedrals in the Midlands collapsed, hundreds of mansions were blown down and thousands of timber framed houses fell. Bricklayers and tilers were able to raise their prices 500 per cent. Enormous damage was done to trees (there were many more then).

Ships were especially badly hit. For as long as anyone could remember there had never been such a concentration of shipping along the south and east coasts of England. During the week before the great storm the weather had been windy everywhere. The ports and harbours were crowded with vessels waiting for the wind to drop. Offshore fleets of naval warships were anchored, along with merchant ships waiting to dock. For five very long hours before sunrise on 8th December there was absolute mayhem along the English Channel and across the southern North Sea. The five-year-old Eddystone lighthouse was swept away; its designer Henry Winstanley was in the lighthouse and perished that night. Ships sank at their moorings; others were blown relentlessly on to the Goodwin Sands. At daybreak twelve men-of-war could be seen wrecked – with 1500 dead. When the wind had died down, Defoe saw a tangle of 700 vessels in the Thames near Limehouse.

Defoe reckoned that about 123 people were killed by the storm in London, and about 8000 throughout the land – although most at sea. In his eyewitness account he recorded that the 'air was full of meteors and vaporous fires' and suggested it was the worst storm ever recorded in history. A good reason for its severity is that it came during the Little Ice Age, when Iceland was surrounded by Arctic sea ice and the temperature change across latitudes just to the south of Britain was very sharp, stimulating severe storm development.

Above and Top Right Low-lying Norfolk was inundated by the floods of 1953. Thousands of acres were flooded; headlines were made and homes evacuated.

Below Many boats were swept onto the coast during the 1953 storm. This boat beached on the Suffolk coast; fortunately the lack of high cliffs in East Anglia meant that most boats remained intact.

1st February 1953

The surge of water that a storm causes is always a threat to coastal parts. Air pressure falls ahead of the storm, alleviating the weight of air pushing down and so allowing the sea level to rise. As the fast moving storm centre sweeps by, so the atmosphere recovers by pushing down hard. This has a plunger effect. A surge of water, a large scale undulation like a wall of water, radiates out on top of the turmoil stirred up on the sea by the rapidly changing fierce winds.

The worst surge of water ever to hit Britain was on 1st February 1953. The storm centre moved down the North Sea, and the gales from the north piled more and more water into the constriction at the southern end of the North Sea. The sea surge on top of high tide overran many sea defences all along the east and south-east coasts of England. At King's Lynn everyone could hear the roaring gale, but no one knew the surge was coming. Suddenly the town centre was flooded by a two metres high wave. High tide at Canvey Island and the Isle of Sheppey was expected about four hours later. About 13,000 people were taken off Canvey Island to safety elsewhere, although fifty-eight were drowned. People trapped on the Isle of Sheppey were rescued by an amphibious vehicle. Luckily for London the high tide lagged the surge of water by about three hours. Nevertheless 307 people were killed by the storm and 30,000 made homeless, and a quarter of a million acres of land were contaminated by salt water.

Left The race against time. The inhabitants of Sea Palling on the East Anglian coast gather to repair their battered sea defences.

16th February 1962

The surge of air that the lie of the land causes during the passage of a storm has produced the most surprising hurricane force winds over Britain.

On 16th February 1962 the storm centre was to the north of Scotland, lashing the northern isles with storm force winds. The mean wind speed recorded in Scotland was lower at around 45 mph. However, at Sheffield in the early hours of the morning the mean speed increased to 75 mph gusting to 95 mph, while just a few miles down the road the mean speed had dropped to 18 mph. In Sheffield whole rows of houses were razed to the ground. Chimney pots were tumbling everywhere. A huge crane was sent crashing into a technical college. A vicarage with stone and brick walls one foot thick was torn apart. At first light the town looked as though it had been blitzed.

Later it was calculated that the Pennines had set the wind undulating in a rare wave motion that had hit Sheffield. The strong airflow from the west was forced up and over the Peak District and then dived down into the Ladbower reservoir valley in the hills, only to be forced up again by the Derwent Moors. To the lee of the moors the undulating wave motion continued as waves do. Unfortunately the horizontal distance from peak to trough was such that Sheffield faced compressed winds in the bottom of the wave trough, while just a few miles away the upwards motion took away the surface wind.

15th January 1968

There was a similar phenomenon on 15th January 1968. This time it was the turn of Glasgow (situated on low ground between mountains) to face the storm winds funnelling up the River Clyde, increasing in strength and in the end touching hurricane force. The 'hurricane' devastated tenements in Patrick and Maryhill. Twenty people were killed and 1700 made homeless, and 100,000 homes were damaged. High tension cables across the Clyde were blown down and so all shipping had to stop until they were cut.

11th August 1979

Storms over the sea are always a lot worse than on land. This is hardly surprising when you consider the lack of shelter at sea; winds have nothing to stop them gathering speed. The sea runs with the wind, fuelling the storm with latent heat. The chaos, the turmoil, the turbulence and the horizontal driving rain are relentless – proof that worse things really do happen at sea. The Fastnet storm on 11th August 1979 over the south-west approaches to Britain whipped up a sea state that was simply overwhelming. On that day over 300 yachts were trying to round Fastnet Rock. Nineteen yachts sank and fifteen yachtsmen drowned; eighty-five yachts made it, and the rest retired.

Left In silence the Fastnet race contestants sail gracefully out of the bay. The blackening skies were the first sign that the elements were about to seal their fate. The latest forecast for the race had flashed a warning of gale force winds to come, but the warning had come too late.

16th October 1987

The infamous 'hurricane' or great October storm devastated the south-east of England. It was the worst storm for 284 years. At the time it was widely thought to be a 'once in a lifetime' event. How wrong that idea was to prove to be.

The great storm of 16th October 1987 was so powerful, so extraordinary, that those affected will always remember where they were that day. The storm came from north-west Spain. On Thursday 15th October at 5 p.m. the eleven metre two-mast boat *Nandisa* lay forty miles off the north-west coast of Spain. The ketch was being delivered to Falmouth by Ron Preedy and John Rencher. Ron writes:

Just when it seemed to me that the wind could not possibly get any stronger, it did precisely that. To the screaming in the rigging was now added a kind of low, unnerving moaning noise. I looked around me awestruck. Visibility was little more than 400 yards, so filled was the air with spray, while secondary waves of about force 4 size were actually climbing up the backs of the huge breakers and peaks that surrounded us. For the next twenty minutes the waves were simply enormous. Being aware of how easy it is to exaggerate when under stress, I remember at one point taking particular care to gauge their height. I can therefore say with absolute certainty that one or two waves were at least 65 feet from crest to trough. Another wave came crashing over me, nearly filling the cockpit. This time I only just managed to keep Nandisa from broaching – and thus quite certainly now, from rolling over. I began to feel desperate.

In England, the trees suffered badly that night because most had lost their leaves, and so presented a large resistance to the storm force wind. Also their roots were less securely anchored than usual because of the waterlogged ground following heavy October rains. The enforced wholescale pruning of woodlands took out fifteen million trees in just one night. People in southern and south-east England woke up to discover that there was no electricity, that trees and roof tiles were lying all over the place in a scene of extensive devastation on a scale greater than any experienced in living memory.

No one could quite believe it. A quarter of Britain was in a state of shock and disbelief. News was hard to come by. The telephone lines to most media centres were down. Broadcasts were hit by power cuts. The Met Office was cut off from the outside world by telephone faults. Slowly it dawned on everyone that they had slept through what the Home Secretary called 'the worst, most widespread night of disaster in the south-east of England since 1945'.

It was also the Met Office's darkest hour. To the person in the street picking up the pieces it was totally inconceivable that the weathermen could have missed the most powerful meteorological storm, about the size of Wales, ever to hit Britain. Nineteen people were killed by the storm; there was plenty of anger at not being warned. On the other hand adversity always brings out the best in the British character. A typical jibe went along the lines: 'We'd lynch all the weathermen if only we could find a tree still standing.'

Right Rendlesham forest in Suffolk, just one of the many forests decimated by the storm.

Left and Below The Royal Botanical Gardens, Kew, London, suffered extensive damage to their collection of rare trees and plants.

Above The October
hurricane peaked during the
night. As a consequence
some heavy sleepers awoke
to the nightmare of finding
their cars flattened by falling
trees.

The storm quickly became widely known as 'the hurricane'. Mean wind speeds above 73 mph, or frequent gusts above 90 mph, are described as hurricane winds. The description fitted the winds over parts of Norfolk, Suffolk, Essex, London, Kent, Surrey, Sussex, Hampshire and the Isle of Wight. The hurricane was at its worst over the widest area between four and five o'clock in the morning, luckily the very time of day with the least number of people out and about. Between one o'clock and six o'clock in the morning the eye of the storm moved from Devon to Lincolnshire with the fiercest winds to the south and east.

The 'hurricane' label was applied when reporters found out that the wind speed had gusted to hurricane force, which seemed only fitting in view of the widespread devastation, never before seen. To call the event merely a storm did not seem dramatic enough. This view was reinforced by the subsequent merciless showing of the previous day's weather broadcast on the BBC. Michael Fish had told viewers: 'Earlier on today, apparently a woman rang the

BBC and said she heard that there was a hurricane on the way. Well if you are watching, don't worry, there isn't.' The nation had found a scapegoat; Michael Fish was to blame!

The media storm that followed was almost as intense as the hurricane. 'The Met Office said there would not be a hurricane, and there was no hurricane' declared the Director General of the Met Office in an interview. *The Sun* called for his resignation, and devoted its front page after the storm to an attractive minor star who unfortunately had had her car squashed. On television the morning after, Jimmy Greaves, who had suffered at the hands of the storm, asserted that 'all these weather presenters care about is appearing on *Blankety Blank*.'

The last television weather forecast before the storm was reviewed, Bill Giles had been on duty and was concerned about 'this quite deep low pressure area. A few days ago we thought it would be coming a little bit further west bringing the strong winds right across the country, but now it looks as though most of the strong winds will stay away, although it's still going to be very breezy up through the Channel and on the eastern side of the country.' During the lunchtime news after the storm Michael Buerk interviewed Ian McCaskill who had been on duty that fateful night at the London Weather Centre, where the observer had been unable to go out on to the roof to take measurements because the wind was so dangerous. This is what was said during the first ever interview of a weatherman:

Buerk: *You chaps were a fat lot of good last night.*

McCaskill: *We have been forecasting hurricane force winds, and that's what we got, and that's what we will get maybe once every fifty years, maybe once every lifetime. We haven't worked out the figures yet.*

Buerk: *Your forecast last night talks about 'a rather windy showery airflow'. No kidding! If you can't forecast the worst storms for several centuries three hours before they happen, what are you doing?*

McCaskill: *Well, we did forecast it rather more than three hours before it happened. Unfortunately that was around midnight, a bit late to tell people. We told everyone we could think of.*

An enquiry into the forecasting of the storm was set up by the Secretary of State for Defence, to whose department the Met Office belongs. The subsequent report found that the lack of warning of the storm was because the computer outputs from the different models of the atmosphere in different countries were not in agreement, and forecasters followed the guidance of their own model too closely, not recognising that on this tricky occasion the wind strength would be way in error. The report stated that no individual should be seriously blamed for the failure to forecast the severity of the storm.

The whole episode had demonstrated the intense interest that the British public has in weather – the great British obsession.

The way in which the great October storm came about was especially interesting, because although it was not a hurricane it was linked to a real hurricane – hurricane Floyd. On 13th October, hurricane Floyd was pounding Miami. The main outflow from the storm was at the top, some nine miles up, and towards the north-east. This extra warm tropical air contrasted sharply with the high altitude polar air it met. When such

Above Walbury, Bracknell, October 1987. A tree uproots and takes the pavement with it. Fifteen million trees in Britain were blown over in just five hours that night.

a plate of warm air tries to overlap the cold air further north, the atmosphere (on our rotating planet) responds by speeding up along the zone of sharpest temperature change. A high altitude fast moving current of air, the jet streak or jet stream, shot across the Atlantic. Over the Bay of Biscay the jet came up against a massive long established heavyweight block of air sitting on Europe which would not give way. The path of least resistance was to turn sharp left and head for Britain.

While all that was happening over the Atlantic, over the Bay of Biscay at lower levels a 'quite deep low pressure area' had formed, and was expected to be steered by the high level flow up the English Channel towards Britain. What followed was that the high level development caught up the low level development, engaged it (like finding a new gear), explosively developed it and then steered it across England. In particular, the high level jet stream was piling air into the sharp left turn it was forced to make, but once through the bend the air could spread out at great speed. There came a time when the spreading out of air could not all be replaced by the weakening upstream jet, and so the underneath air was forced to rise up to take its place. But underneath there was already a quite deep low pressure area with its typical strong ascent. These two previously separate features coupled to create an exceptionally strong ascent of air, alleviating the weight of air pushing down, causing the low pressure centre to rapidly become even lower in pressure.

This 'explosive deepening' of the low pressure centre was the trigger for the hurricane force winds. Air wants to blow directly from high pressure to low pressure, as when a car tyre bursts. The harder the tyre is pumped up, the more violent the rush out when it bursts. On a larger scale, on our rotating planet, air suffers a deflecting force – the Coriolis force – which makes it spiral around a low pressure centre. The greater the pressure change, the faster the wind spirals in. Explosive deepening causes the greatest pressure change and thus the strongest swirling winds. While all that was happening the exceptionally strong ascent of air was taking a lot of the warm Biscay waters into the sky and eventually condensing them into clouds. For every gram of water vapour that condenses, 600 calories of latent heat are released. The enormous release of latent heat in the storm made the rising air even more buoyant, strengthening the ascent even more. The whole thing was a bomb being steered into England. The rest is history.

Above A pathetic scene at Littlehampton in October 1987. Beach huts along the promenade were flattened by the wind.

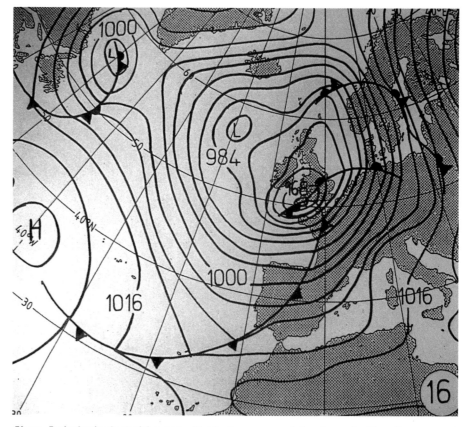

Above An isobaric chart of the storm. The isobars are most closely packed together over southern and south-eastern England. The winds there reached over 100 mph.

Left The small village of Long Stratton in Norfolk was severely damaged by a freak tornado on the 14th December 1989. There had been a spate of thunderstorms in the area which probably led to the tornado.

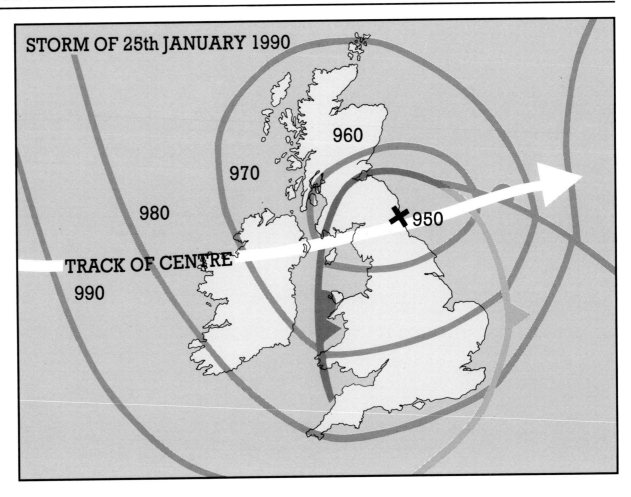

STORM OF 25th JANUARY 1990

960

970

980

X 950

TRACK OF CENTRE

990

Right The eye of the storm moved west to east – with the strongest winds on its southern flank.

25th January 1990

Early in 1990 an amazing sequence of storms lashed the British Isles and northern Europe, leaving a trail of death, destruction and flooding. The great British obsession blazed a trail through all the media. Newspapers, radio and television demanded to know what was happening to our weather. Has our weather gone berserk? Is our climate changing? Is the greenhouse effect to blame? Nobody knew why storm after storm suddenly lashed Britain, yet everyone speculated, the stories about the storms were prolific.

The sequence of storms began on Thursday morning, 25th January 1990. Teleprinters around the country simultaneously purred out a message:

Here is a flash message of severe weather issued by the Met Office at 0615 GMT on 25th January 1990. South-westerly winds will soon increase to storm force over south-west England, and severe gales will extend to south Wales, central, southern and south-east England during the morning. Gusts will be in excess of 90 mph near the coast and 70 mph inland. Some structural damage may occur before winds moderate later this afternoon.

Experience of hurricanes hitting the USA has shown that winds going over 80 mph are usually those that cause structural damage. The same was all too vividly seen (and filmed) that fateful Thursday in Britain. The critical threshold for roofs taking off appears to be 80 mph, and it's the gusts that do the damage. Since the pressure exerted by the wind on something depends on the square of the speed, just a small increase in wind speed greatly increases its destructive capability.

While the forecast that day turned out to be not quite right, not precisely correct, it was reasonably accurate. Winds of 100 mph battered the south coast of Wales and south coast of England. Storm force winds gusting 70 mph were commonplace over England, Wales, southern Ireland and southern Scotland. Most of Scotland, from 56.5°N northwards had a relatively quiet day.

The strongest recorded gust was 107 mph at Aberporth in south Wales. This compares with the strongest wind at near sea level (disregarding mountain top gusts) ever recorded in Britain of 140 mph at Fraserburgh in north Scotland on 13th February 1989. It's a curious thing that the many winds that have topped 107 mph over Scotland this century have hardly ever had a mention in the newspapers, whereas a storm over southern England is the lead story for days on end.

The death toll reached forty-six, the number of trees down was around three million, the number of homes without electricity ran into hundreds of thousands, and the insurance companies put the cost at more than £2 billion. Most of the deaths were caused by falling trees. Many more were injured by flying glass, roadside hoardings, tiles and scaffolding.

In the news that week there had been stories of the warmest winter for 331 years. On 23rd January 1990 the *Daily Mail*'s headline was 'Just the weather to put a spring in your step'. The story began: 'The daffodils and buttercups

THE DAWN OF SPRING IN OUR SUBURB
Study of two romantic natures rising superior to their environment.

are bursting into bloom. Birds are beginning to nest. Hungry hedgehogs just don't want to hibernate, and it's all thanks to the warmest winter for 331 years – since before the restoration of Charles II'. Just two days later the storm hit, and 'havoc' was 'wreaked' in the same newspaper. 'Havoc' was also wreaked in *The Daily Telegraph*. 'Deadly havoc' was wreaked in *The*

Left A casualty of the storm force winds over south-west England, 25th January 1990.

Guardian, whereas *The Times* saw 'winds of devastation'. The *Daily Star* saw 'the wind of death' as its headline, beginning its account: 'A horror hurricane turned southern Britain into a scene from a disaster movie yesterday.'

Everyone is used to national newspaper headline overkill, but still many people must have been bemused by 'killer hurricane', 'mayhem' and 'panic' when their own experience was seeing a few dustbins blown over and a few tiles on the pavements.

The *Today* newspaper went further. 'Criminal' ran its headline as it joined the 'why weren't we warned?' brigade. The story read: 'Yesterday's hurricane was predicted in advance, but the warnings given by the weathermen were so feeble they did not merit any significant show in national newspapers, read by most of the country. Bland TV forecasts earlier this week also gave little hint of the carnage which would be wrought. Last night we were paying the price of that folly, as the hurricane raged.'

Leaving aside the fact that the storm was not a hurricane, and not bothering to challenge the assertion that most people in the land read those newspapers, the crucial point is: were warnings of severe winds given? The answer has to be 'yes'. Just because *Today* chose to be one of the FADS (forget action until disaster strikes), and so had no forecast of the storm, doesn't mean that the weathermen were to blame. What do people expect? A carnage scale to go with the Beaufort scale?

What is truly remarkable is that the forecast was so close to reality. After all, nobody lives in the Atlantic where the storm came from. Nobody knew precisely what was happening out there. Weathermen have satellites and computers, but that doesn't mean they can see what is going on over the Atlantic. The computers have to be fed with that information first, and then they can do something useful with it. The satellites can't see through high cloud. They cannot see the ground truth. At night they cannot see anything; they sense the thermal map of the highest clouds over the Atlantic. Who knows exactly what is brewing underneath?

People are much too quick nowadays to expect every weather forecast to be accurate because of all the high technology used. The plain truth is that planet earth, which should really be called 'planet ocean', has vast uninhabited areas where it is impossible to remotely sense exactly what is going on. The errors that this fact introduces into the subsequent forecast sequences simply grow and grow, or 'snowball'.

Below **After the Severn in Worcester burst its banks the only things able to pass this point were the swans.**

Forecasting is still not an exact science. Just like medicine, there is a certain art involved as well.

While weathermen began to agree to include in their forecasts references to roofs being blown off, and whether people should stay at home or not, the next storm was brewing out in the Atlantic. No one knew that an exceptionally stormy period had begun.

1st February 1990

The next storm hit Britain one week later, on Thursday 1st February 1990. The track of the storm centre, the 'eye' of the storm, was different. The January storm centre had swept due west to east across the middle of Britain. Consequently the most violent winds were over southern Britain (to the south of the storm centre) where the circulating wind added to the progressive wind speed. The first February storm centre tracked north-eastwards past the Outer Hebrides. Consequently the most violent winds hit Ireland and the north-west half of Scotland – the very places that the January storm had missed. Northern Ireland had severe blizzards and north-west Scotland was deluged by driving rain on the Friday. That same rain belt had put vast areas of the English west country under water, and in the process cut off hundreds of

Left A common sight in the west country after the storm.

Above Come hell or high water the great British public keep the flag flying!

"If you're so fond of the goldfish, Ruby, why don't you come down and help me to look for them?"

thousands of homes from electricity and telephones where they had only just been restored. The gritty smiles and the stoical shrugs for the benefit of the news crews were beginning to look a bit hollow.

3rd February 1990

Worse was to come. During Friday 2nd and Saturday 3rd February 1990 yet another storm swirled in from the Atlantic. This time the track of the storm centre was along the English Channel. Consequently, this time the strongest winds hit France. The worst gales there in living memory left twenty-three dead. At one point the wind blew from Brighton to Dieppe at 100 mph. As the storm moved along the Channel the winds on its northern flank were not so severe as with the previous storms, but amazingly heavy rain fell over the southern half of England. For a few hours the first falls of snow that winter fell over Oxfordshire, Wiltshire, Berkshire, Dorset, Hampshire, Buckinghamshire, Bedfordshire and Hertfordshire but within six hours most of southern England had two centimetres of rain. That's like 200 tonnes of water tipped on to

every field or estate the size of a football pitch. It meant that some southern counties of England from Sussex to Cornwall had soaked up four inches of rain (about five weeks' normal rainfall at that time of year) in just eight days.

The Severn, Avon and Thames valleys were flooded in parts when rivers swollen by torrential rain burst their banks. Gloucestershire had its worst floods for forty-three years, after the River Severn rose fourteen feet above normal. Upton upon Severn became Severn upon Upton; youngsters went wind-surfing down the high street, and publicans fished out salmon swimming passed their front door. Despite all the floods, Lee Valley Water confounded everybody by warning customers in Hertfordshire, Bedfordshire, Essex and north London that they should be careful over water consumption, or face the prospect of a hosepipe ban in the summer. A sense of humour through times of devastation is a wonderful thing, but in reality the phlegmatic householders of south-west England were being severely tested. The weather, normally something of a joke, had become a very serious matter indeed.

The insurance companies began reassessing the risk of storm damage to property. The rush of storm claims was now, after more storms, likely to top £3 billion, and so a 25 per cent rise in premium rates might be justified, especially if the climate was changing. Nobody could answer that. While the insurance companies debated, the elements had not finished with Britain. Yet more storms were on the way.

7th February 1990

Four days later in the small hours of Wednesday morning, 7th February 1990, storm force winds were buffeting the south of England. An extreme gust of 96 mph was recorded at Berry Head. This early morning storm had somehow slipped through the net unannounced, and its driving rain was compounding problems in the Thames valley, especially around Maidenhead, where the weekend floods were still evident. What was clear, though, was that yet another storm was closing in fast, hard on the heels of the current chaos. At 0625 GMT Wednesday morning the Met Office flashed:

Vigorous low will track across central southern Scotland tonight bringing severe gales to much of the UK, although if the track remains as predicted northern

Scotland should miss the worst of the wind. Coastal areas will be worst affected, especially southern and western areas with mean speeds 45 to 60 mph in places and gusts 70 to 90 mph. Further heavy rain today and tonight will exacerbate existing high river levels.

As it turned out, Scotland and Ireland missed the strong winds. The 45 to 65 mph winds hit west Wales and most of southern England. A few inland areas had gales, and notably Heathrow equalled its highest ever gust for February with 70 mph. Everyone had been expecting the worst, because the early warning was issued at the very time there were already gales blowing. After the events of previous weeks all the emergency services, and the army, were standing by on red alert.

During Thursday morning, 8th February, it was clear that the gusts to 90 mph had not happened. Consequently some radio interviewers began to question whether the strength of winds was overdone. At the same time the MP for Beckenham wrote to the chairman of the BBC claiming that the BBC's weather warnings were 'astonishingly inadequate'. The truth of the matter was that throughout an exceptionally difficult fast changing weather fortnight, individual extreme weather events were handled with

great skill. Forecasts that were reasonably accurate and timely (though not perfect) had helped many people and probably saved lives.

Meteorologists had been dragged through the fortnight by a jet stream, with hardly time to draw breath. A tranquil spell was badly needed. The atmosphere had other ideas. In fact February 1990 was to become one of the most notable months of the century. All sorts of records were broken across Britain, against the background of a generally wet and windy month. For example, Scotland from Glasgow up to Fort William had its wettest ever month on record. In London alone the following records were set:

- Highest February day maximum temperature since 1961, at 18.5°C on the 23rd.

- Highest February night minimum temperature since 1960, at 12.0°C on the 24th.

- Highest February average day maximum temperature since records began, at 11.7°C.

- Highest February mean temperature for more than 200 years, at 9.4°C.

- Highest February gust since 1984.

- Highest February rainfall since 1979.

- Highest mean monthly wind speed since records began.

Below A big surprise was awaiting the pilot of this light aircraft – another expensive casualty of the storm.

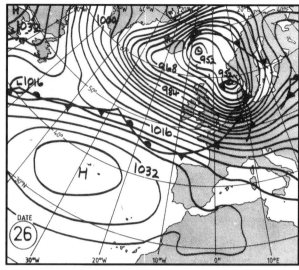

Above An isobaric chart of the February Storm

26th February 1990

Still the elements raged. Just three days after parts of Britain had their hottest February day this century, storm force winds gusting to 100 mph swept in from the Atlantic across Britain and into The Netherlands, France, Belgium, Germany and Switzerland. One of the warmest, wettest and windiest Februarys ever known in Britain certainly 'went out like a lion'. Roaring winds combined with the highest tides of the year wrought the worst destruction the town of Towyn on the north Wales coast had ever seen.

The storm of 26th February 1990 was accurately forecast. The timing was right, the wind strength was right and the rainfall was right. But what no one foresaw was the Victorian sea defences at Towyn being tossed aside by the Irish Sea. As the storm centre passed over Wales on its way to Holland the extra low pressure alleviated the weight of air pushing down on the sea, allowing the sea to rise. To the rear of the storm centre, as the atmosphere recovered by pushing down hard, a surge of water driven by fierce winds arrived at the north Wales resort on top of the highest tide of the year. Huge breakers slammed into the crumbling sea defences, causing devastation and severe flooding.

Left Towyn, north Wales.
The transformation of
caravans to houseboats!

Left The RSPCA were kept busy by saving many stranded pets during the floods.

Left Workmen rush to repair the sea wall at Towyn before the next high tide.

That particular storm also caused serious coastal flooding in Blackpool, Morecambe, Fleetwood, Appledore, Bideford, Ilfracombe, Lynmouth, Worthing, Hastings, Dymchurch, Folkestone, Hythe, Sandgate, Camber and St Mary's Bay. The trail of destruction left eighteen dead in Britain and twenty-eight dead on the Continent.

Searching back through weather records, the easiest conclusion to reach about all the storms that have wrought death and destruction on Britain is that they are all simply part of the grand natural variability of climate. We have always had severe storms, we will always get severe storms, and of course we will be eternally startled by severe storms. The history books record that the Goodwin Sands off the east coast of Kent were dry land until a storm in the eleventh century swamped them. The Saxon town of Selsey in Sussex was overwhelmed and washed into the sea. In 1287 the port of Old Winchelsea near Rye was swept into the sea by a severe storm. The same storm battered Dunwich on the Suffolk coast between Southwold and Aldeburgh. Houses and ships were swept into the sea, and Britain's fifth most prosperous port slipped into decline. Another severe storm pounded the town in 1328, and the port never recovered.

Perhaps there is some order in the natural variability of climate. Some climatologists have suggested a cyclic pattern of severe storms every hundred years. Particularly stormy weather affected Britain, some believe, in the 1590s, 1690s, 1790s and 1890s. The statistical data are patchy and questionable. It is always easy to find cycles if you are allowed to select the facts that suit you. However, if true the 1990s should be exceptionally stormy. Even less clear is the mechanism behind the cycle. Solar disturbances have always been a favourite with fringe scientists, and can be made to correlate with a wide range of events. But the common denominator is that the link between the event and the sunspot can never be shown. The climate probably does vary over many different cycles. Sometimes the cycles overlap constructively, and sometimes they interfere destructively to cancel each other out. Sorting out the muddle is like trying to sort out the notes from a single instrument when the whole orchestra is playing.

High seas pounding the 'golden mile' at Blackpool, Lancashire.

On the other hand there is something unnerving about the storms of recent times. Perhaps we are entering a Wind Age of a more hostile kind. Perhaps the atmosphere, by sending us a whole batch of severe storms so soon after the 'hurricane' of 1987, is trying to tell us something. Perhaps we are changing the climate, and the apparent increases in the frequency of severe storms and all sorts of other extreme weather events are the first symptoms of that change. Maybe in the next century we will look back to now and say, 'Yes, that was the first sign.'

Two storms don't make a greenhouse effect, but the link cannot be ruled out. Are storms increasing owing to the greenhouse effect? Will mankind's exploits reap a stormy reaction from the atmosphere?

The greenhouse effect is real. We really are contaminating the atmosphere more and more each year. There are a host of theories ranging from 'the greenhouse effect must mean more storms' to 'the greenhouse effect must mean less storms'.

At the simplest level, a warming world that warms more over the polar regions than the equator will reduce the temperature contrast from equator to pole. For Britain it is the strong temperature contrast across the Atlantic Ocean, from north to south, that causes storms to develop. If this contrast is reduced then any storms that do develop in the zone of strongest temperature gradient will be less intense. Taking this information as granted then it looks like the threat of extreme storms would be reduced.

The sudden upsurge in severe storms lashing Britain then, must be nothing more than part of the grand natural variability of weather across these islands. Or is it? What about the 'hurricane' of 1987 being a 'once in a lifetime event'? Maybe the track of the intense depressions has changed.

Past records show that intense depressions (or storms) typically run from the mid Atlantic to Norway passing between Iceland and Scotland. That's why the north of Scotland, on the periphery of such storms, can at times be a wild place to live. The storms are steered that way by the jet stream. Jet streams occur because the world is differentially heated by the sun, whilst rotating. For example, Britain rotates at about 600 mph west to east. The atmosphere responds by producing jetstreams. These are high altitude, fast currents of air that wriggle their

their way west to east from America to Europe, dragging the underlying weather across the lands they travel over. The axis of the jet forms along the line of strongest temperature contrast; where the plate of tropical high level air overlaps the polar air. With increased global warming it is entirely possible that the axis of the jet will lie, on average over more southern latitudes. Therefore more depressions will be steered across Britain and the Continent. Some of those depressions will no doubt be intense. So, the general perception will be an increase in the occurrence of extreme weather events.

It should also be remembered that although we talk about global warming, there are in reality large regional variations. For example, while the atmosphere as a whole has warmed up, the eastern USA and Canada is colder, as is the north Pacific Ocean. These cooler regions may not stay that way; so, as hot and cold regions try to average out (as the world warms unevenly), it is likely that more severe storms will develop in the areas of strong temperature contrast. So the greenhouse effect may well create storms from new regions. In winter when the axis of the jet stream quite naturally shifts to more southern latitudes the track of these storms could be into Britain.

However, as far as the sequence of storms in early 1990 are concerned there is no evidence to show that the temperature gradient across the north Atlantic Ocean was any stronger than it has been before – that's the problem. Even though a small amount of global warming has happened, most of it is due to the heating of the southern hemisphere oceans, which, because of their inertia are the last places to expect warming to occur. So the greenhouse effect cannot explain why more storms should lash Britain. Nor can sun-spots because the amount of energy involved is minute compared with those that heat the earth.

However it is interesting that the 1980s were the warmest decade on record, and globally there were record extreme weather events, like hurricane Gilbert. It is well known that warm air can hold more water vapour than cold air. More water vapour in the air means more latent heat energy available to fuel the storm. After all, every gramme of water vapour in the wind that condenses into cloud releases 600 calories of heat. This is a potentially enormous source of energy bound to make for more intense storms.

In the end it is just not possible to explain the events of January and February 1990. On the premise that you are innocent until proven guilty the greenhouse effect should be cleared of all charges relating to the storms – but I have my doubts.

Below The most striking feature seen from space in our atmosphere is a jet stream. It is a fast moving current of high altitude wind that wiggles its way around each hemisphere.

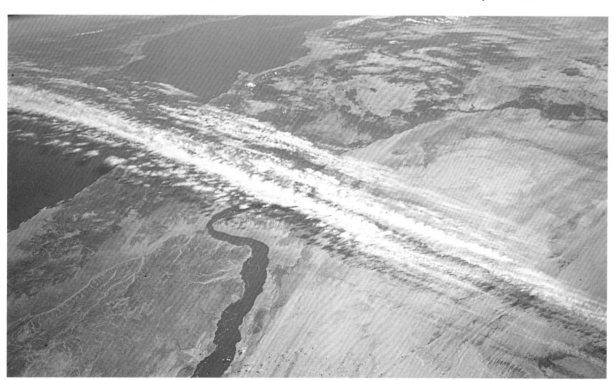

Mr. Editor!
Whenever there comes a big storm, there are two or three gentlemen who at once write off to *The Times*, just as if it had rained, hailed, thundered, and lightened for them alone. They always seem to think that they have been on the very spot where the storm was at its worst, and yet, after all, they never tell of more than an inch or so of rain falling. In our part of the country we do not think much of an inch, I can tell you. Why, I have often had it knee-deep in the dip in the road by my house, and yet I have never written to the editor of *The Times*. Now, Sir, what I want you people in London to understand is this. The worst part of this storm was in this here parish......

Punch 1879

METEOROLOGY AND THE WEATHER FORECAST

Old men and comets have been reverenced
for the same reason; their long beards,
and pretences to foretell events.

Jonathan Swift, *Faculties of the Mind (1709)*

A WEATHER WAIL.
"I wonder whether, bless your eyes,
  Can any man be weather-wise!"–*Songs of a Sangarorum.*

Meteorology – the science of weather – is a subject that is continually progressing. For hundreds of years we have been inventing new methods to forecast our weather. As soon as one invention was found along came another even better. The race is on for the most accurate and up to date forecast – however the race is by no means over and it is debatable as to whether it ever will be.

Although modern science only really began to flourish in the 1600s, there was one period of 300 years or so, in Ancient Greece, when intellectual freedom and an equable weather climate allowed science to flourish. However, before this period it was generally believed that the weather was mythical as opposed to scientific.

At first the Greeks thought of the winds as gods. The world's greatest monument to the weather is the Tower of the Winds, which was built in the market place of Athens and is still standing today. Each of the eight sides of the tower was sculpted to show the character of the wind from that direction.

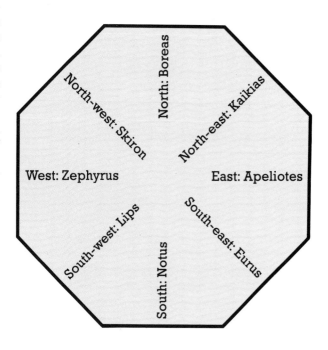

Right The Tower of the Winds. This hexagonal building was built in Athens.

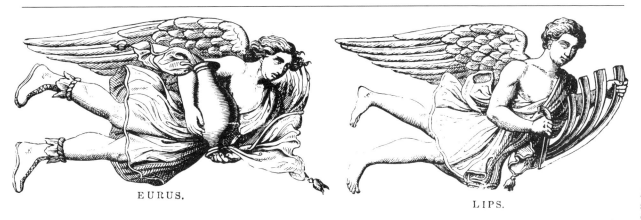

E U R U S.

LIPS.

Left Eurus, God of the south-east wind and Lips, God of the south-west wind.

The Empire of the Winds was shared between the four sons of Eos – Boreas, Zephyrus, Eurus and Notus – who represent the four main winds. Boreas was represented as a winged man of mature age with long hair floating in the wind. It was said that Boreas assumed the form of a stallion to mate with twelve of the mares of Erichthonius. From this union were born twelve fillies, so light of step that they 'ran across fields of standing corn without bruising an ear of grain and over the crests of the sea without wetting their feet.' Boreas lived in the caves of the wild mountainous area of Thrace along with his brother Zephyrus. Originally Zephyrus – God of the West Wind – was a savage and baleful wind, who enjoyed making hurricanes and causing havoc at sea. Later Zephyrus's violent disposition calmed and he became a soft and gentle wind, whose breath awoke the spring flowers from their winter slumber.

As for the other gods, their individualities were never really defined as they were deemed to be lesser gods.

By the time of Aristotle, the Greek civilisation had progressed to believe that the weather elements were not under the personal control of the gods, but rather – as Aristotle pointed out in his treatise *Meteorologica* – were caused by the sun. Mysticism, myth and religion gave way to science. The appeal of science comes from being able to rely on laws which do not tangibly exist but which can be verified by constantly recurring facts. Myth, on the other hand, is just based on unverified notions that might by chance represent what actually happens.

Aristotle was convinced that air was weightless. He filled a leather bag with air and weighed it. He pressed the bag flat and then reweighed it – no difference! Therefore he came to the conclusion that air weighed nothing.

The centuries rolled by. Then in 1640 the Grand Duke of Tuscany wanted to build a garden fountain. No matter how hard he tried using a suction pump, he couldn't raise the water in the ground by more than thirty-two feet

Left Zephyrus, God of the west wind and Apeliotes, God of the east wind.

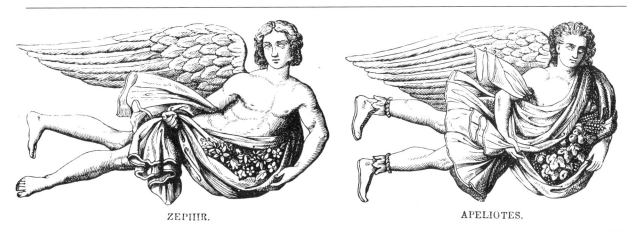

ZEPHIR.

APELIOTES.

is, mercury in a tube will rise or fall to a point where it is in equilibrium with the weight of the atmosphere over the same base. In other words he had invented the barometer.

So now when we notice a change in the mercury level we know that the weight of air pressing down on our heads has changed. When the level in the glass falls (depressed) we say that a depression is coming, although, as Louis MacNeice writes in *Bagpipe Music*:

The glass is falling hour by hour,
the glass will fall for ever,
But if you break the bloody glass
you won't hold up the weather.

Louis MacNeice

At about the same time, the Grand Duke of Tuscany made the first sealed thermometer using the expansion and contraction of alcohol in a glass tube. However, because alcohol boils before water, the thermometer had limited uses. The first mercury thermometers were produced by the Accademia del Cimento at Florence in 1657.

In 1714 the German physicist Gabriel Fahrenheit invented a scale of temperature. On his scale the melting point of ice was 32°F and

Above Torricelli, by watching the level of mercury in his glass tube, could tell the air pressure changes.

Top Right Modern day barometers function without the use of mercury and are called aneroid barometers.

The Duke wrote to Galileo about it, who passed the problem on to his pupil, Torricelli. Torricelli saw that the whole weight of the atmosphere pressing down on the water reservoir must be balanced by a column of water thirty-two feet high. By replacing water with mercury in his experiment to prove this, Torricelli actually invented a way of measuring air pressure: that

Left Perhaps Hooke found inspiration for the anemometer from his local pub!

the boiling point of water was 212°F. This was far too involved for the Swedish astronomer Anders Celsius, who invented a scale which had 100°C as the melting point of ice and 0°C as the boiling point of water. In the 1740s this was reversed by understandably popular demand.

About the same time that the barometer and thermometer were invented, Robert Hooke was developing an idea sketched out by Leonardo da Vinci to measure wind. Hooke made a metal plate hinged at the top, rather like a pub sign, enabling it to swing alongside a curved scale: the stronger the wind, the greater the swing. The first cup anemometer was invented by John Robinson in 1846. It consisted of three or four cups in the horizontal plane, pivoted on a vertical spindle: the stronger the wind, the more revolutions per minute.

So with the invention of the barometer, the thermometer and the anemometer in the seventeenth and eighteenth centuries, a new era had begun. Meteorology had been lifted from the realms of myth to the status of a science. Further discoveries followed. In 1648 came the final confirmation that air has weight when the French physicist, Blaise Pascal sent his brother up the Puy-de-Dôme mountain carrying a mercury barometer. The mercury level fell seven and a half centimetres during the 1500 metre climb, proving that the instrument was measuring the weight of the air. His findings are now well known as Pascal's principle or Pascal's law.

In 1862 James Glaisher rose to 11,500 metres in a basket underneath a hydrogen filled balloon, measuring the profiles of temperature and atmospheric pressure. In the process he was almost asphyxiated and was obliged to pull the string of the descent valve with his teeth!

In 1752 the American Benjamin Franklin attached a key to the end of his kite string and flew it into the centre of a thunderstorm. When he offered his knuckle to the key, a spark jumped on to his hand. Franklin had discovered that lightning was electricity.

Above In 1862 James Glaisher's ascent in a balloon almost ended in disaster when he was almost asphyxiated.

Rain has always been the easiest weather element to collect and measure. Christopher Wren made the first rain collector that automatically emptied when full. From 1677 to 1703 Richard Towneley kept a continuous record of the rainfall at Towneley Hall, near Burnley.

Sir Francis Beaufort devised a wind scale in 1805, based on the speed that a well maintained man-of-war would make. It is still in use today in a revised version. You will notice in the picture of the Beaufort Scale below, that I have added the mean wind speed, the maximum height of waves and the state of the sea.

In theory, then, Britain's weather records go back to about the mid 1600s. It was possible for people to measure air pressure, temperature and wind speeds, to record things like visibility and the amount and types of cloud, and generally to observe what the weather was doing. Unfortunately, finding such records proves very difficult. This sort of hobby was for the intelligentsia, and so observers were pretty scarce.

In 1820 Henrich Brandes conceived the idea of putting all the weather observations taken simultaneously in various parts of the country onto one broad view map. He made the first weather map of synoptic (all seen together) observations. However instead of lines of equal pressure (isobars) Brandes drew, for reasons best known to himself, lines of equal deviation from 'normal'.

The year 1844 saw the first electric telegraph commercial network in the USA; yet

Above To get accurate readings, rain gauges have to be placed well away from buildings, trees and most of all dogs!

Above Sir Francis Beaufort, creator of the renowned 'Beaufort scale'.

Beaufort scale: specifications and equivalent speeds

Force	Description	Specification for use at sea*	Equivalent speed at 10m above ground knots		Description in forecasts	State of sea	Probable height of waves* metres
			Mean	Limits			
0	Calm	Sea like a mirror.	0	>1	Calm	Calm	0.0
1	Light air	Ripples with the appearance of scales are formed, but without foam crests.	2	1-3	Light	Calm	0.1 (0.1)
2	Light breeze	Small wavelets, still short but more pronounced. Crests have a glassy appearance and do not break.	5	4-6	Light	Smooth	0.2 (0.3)
3	Gentle breeze	Large wavelets. Crests begin to break. Foam of glassy appearance. Perhaps scattered white horses.	9	7-10	Light	Smooth	0.6 (1.0)
4	Moderate breeze	Small waves, becoming longer, fairly frequent white horses.	13	11-16	Moderate	Slight	1.0 (1.5)
5	Fresh breeze	Moderate waves, taking a more pronounced long form; many white horses are formed. Chance of some spray.	19	17-21	Fresh	Moderate	2.0 (2.5)
6	Strong breeze	Large waves begin to form; the white foam crests are more extensive everywhere. Probably some spray.	24	22-27	Strong	Rough	3.0 (4.0)
7	Near gale	Sea heaps up and white foam from breaking waves begins to be blown in streaks along the direction of the wind.	30	28-33	Strong	Very rough	4.0 (5.5)
8	Gale	Moderately high waves of greater length; edges of crests begin to break into spindrift. The foam is blown in well-marked streaks along the direction of the wind.	37	34-40	Gale	High	5.5 (7.5)
9	Strong gale	High waves. Dense streaks of foam along the direction of the wind. Crests of waves begin to topple, tumble and roll over. Spray may affect visibility.	44	41-47	Severe gale	Very high	7.0 (10.0)
10	Storm	Very high waves with long overhanging crests. The resulting foam, in great patches, is blown in dense white streaks along the direction of the wind. On the whole the surface of the sea takes a white appearance. the 'tumbling' of the sea becomes heavy and shock-like. Visibility affected.	52	48-55	Storm	Very high	9.0 (12.5)
11	Violent storm	Exceptionally high waves (small and medium-sized ships mightbe for a time lost to view behind the waves). The sea is completely covered with long white patches of foam lying along the direction of the wind. Everywhere the edges of the wave crests are blown into froth. Visibility affected.	60	56-63	Violent storm	Phenomenal	11.5 (16.0)
12	Hurricane	The air is filled with foam and spray. Sea completely white with driving spray; visibility very seriously affected.	–	>64	Hurricane force	Phenomenal	14.0 (–)

Above Admiral Fitzroy, first head of the Meteorological Department founded by the British Government in 1855.

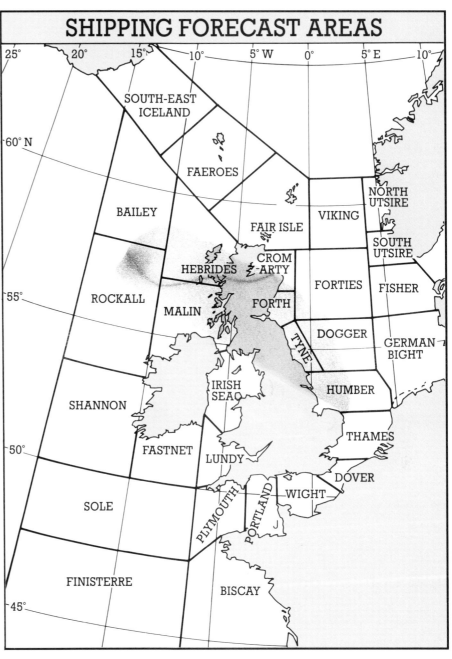

SHIPPING FORECAST AREAS

Above In 1859 Admiral Fitzroy was authorised to produce the first shipping forecast. The shipping areas as shown above have become familiar to us all thanks to Radio 4's daily shipping forecast.

England was the first country to publish a daily weather map on the same day that the information was received. By 1855 the British Government had set up the Meteorological Department with responsibility for collecting all the weather observations it could. In a debate on the department, one member of Parliament anticipated that in a few years' time 'We might know in this metropolis, the condition of the weather twenty-four hours beforehand.' There followed much laughter.

Admiral Fitzroy, head of the Meteorological Department, did not find such things funny. For years he had been advocating a storm warning service for coastal shipping, and in 1859, when a storm off Anglesey sank the *Royal Charter*, he was authorised to do just that. By noting pressure changes, wind speeds and temperatures at twenty different locations each morning, Fitzroy somehow or other managed to come up with what he called forecasts for up to two days in advance. The first forecasts for the public were issued to the press in July 1861. Controversy reigned from day one of the forecasts and the debate generated strong feelings on all sides. It was obviously all too much for Fitzroy who, on 30th April 1865, committed suicide by cutting his throat with his razor.

As yet no other head or director general of the Met Office has taken that way out. In fact today the Met Office is highly regarded as a centre of scientific excellence, even though its forecasts are fallible. For example, the Met Office has never been sued for negligence by

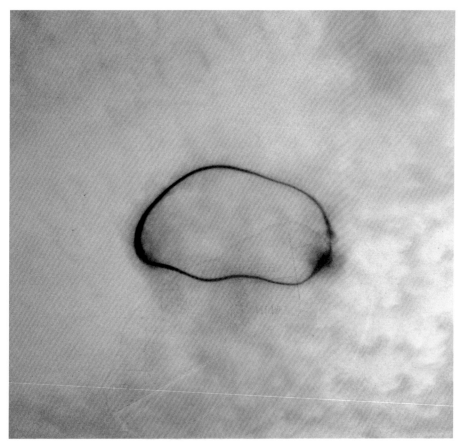

Above Anyone who has watched smoke from a bonfire will know that air moves in swirls. This large smoke ring was spotted beneath the clouds over Fife, proving that there are indeed larger whirls all around us.

Right Lewis F. Richardson whose weather forecasting dream became a reality.

time cascade up through the scales of motions and eddies and swirls in the atmosphere to ultimately affect the track of a great storm. This relatively new train of thought is called chaos theory. The inherent chaos in the turbulent motions of the atmosphere means that, in practice, there is a limit beyond which the atmosphere is unpredictable. Isn't that a comforting thought? No matter how hard anyone tries, the weather will never be totally predictable.

Richardson had a complex fantasy which he expressed in terms of a weather factory. A shift of 64,000 workers would come in and take their seats. The inside of the factory building would be painted to represent the world. The workers would spread out evenly across the world, some over the Atlantic, some on Australia and so on. To simplify his vision, if it was possible to process the information from 64,000 points throughout the world fast enough – that is, before the change in weather overtakes the calculations – it would be possible to forecast the weather with the minimum amount of error. In the 1920s Richardson wrote: *'Perhaps someday in the future it will be possible to advance*

any of its clients, presumably because the Great British public understands that weather forecasts, like doctors' diagnoses, are not infallible. Nevertheless, the quest is on to produce totally accurate forecasts day after day after day.

A quantum leap towards accurate forecasting was made by Lewis Richardson in his book *Weather Prediction by Numerical Process*, published in 1922. Regarding all the interactions of all the turbulent motions from smoke rings to cyclones in the atmosphere, he wrote:

Big whirls have little whirls
that feed on their velocity,
And little whirls have lesser whirls
and so on to viscosity –
In the molecular sense.

As the cascade theory to which he alludes works both ways, he might have added:

And the big whirls themselves in turn,
have bigger whirls to go on
While these again have greater still and
greater still and so on.

Meteorologists have found that, in theory, the flap of a butterfly's wings in a garden may in

LEWIS F. RICHARDSON, D.Sc., F.R.S.
Pioneer in numerical weather forecasting.

the computations faster than the weather advances and at a cost less than the saving to mankind due to the information gained. But that is a dream.'

Today that dream is a reality. Instead of people at each grid point, we employ electronic devices. Observations from all over the world are fed into a computer to set values for all the weather elements. The computer is pro-grammed to put those values into its equations and solve them for the initial rate of change. This tells us the new value of the weather elements at the end of a brief period, say ten minutes. The computer takes the new values as if they were the initial set and does the same thing all over again. We advance another ten minutes – and so on.

Left The butterfly effect is that the vortices spun off the flap of its wings move invisibly through the air to interact with other swirls and cascade up through the scales of motion. So in theory the end result could be to change the course of the weather.

So, a computer forecast for twenty-four hours ahead is made up of 144 calculations or time steps – 144 opportunities for the tiny errors in the initial set of values to grow and grow. To minimise the errors, both the grid length and the time step must be as small as possible; but that would mean the computer would have an impossible number of things to do. In any case we do not have the capability to observe the atmosphere in such fine detail, especially over the oceans. Clearly the initial values, observations and analysis are vital in producing a good forecast. The more accurate the analysis of weather, the more accurate the weather forecast.

In Richardson's day the analysis was by guess and by God. Today we can tell whether there are clouds over the Atlantic or not, we can even see what is going on in remote areas at frequent intervals, all because of satellites. As well as pictures, satellites can give a rough idea about the vertical distribution of wind and temperature through the atmosphere. The weather satellite then is a tremendous aid to the analysis; on which everything else depends.

Weather satellites started in 1960. There are now two sorts: one is 530 miles up and the other is 22,370 miles out in space. The lower type is called a polar orbiting satellite because it orbits from pole to pole every 100 minutes. The pictures we get back are of the strip of earth over which the satellite has passed. On its next orbit it will cover a different strip because the planet rotates through some 25° longitude in

Below The pole to pole orbiting satellite shows us the snow on the Alps and Norwegian mountains on a virtually clear day over Europe.

Above This magnified shot of Britain tells the forecasters that the weather will be sunny and dry. Aberdeen down through Fife to Berwick though, will have coastal fog.

Right This satellite image of the reflected sunlight shows sea fog rolling onto the east coast from Humberside northwards.

100 minutes. The Russians even set a pair of satellites orbiting almost together, presumably to get a 3-D view of the clouds. The images of the clouds were recorded from slightly different angles by the two satellites and then passed through different colour filters; when viewed with colour filter spectacles, they would give a good impression of the relative depth of the clouds.

The high type of satellite is known as geo-stationary because it remains at a fixed point over the earth, but moves with the earth through its twenty-four hour cycle. Because the satellite sits over the equator, the picture is clearest there, but it becomes squashed and muddled towards the poles because the earth is sloping away from the satellite. The great thing about our geostationary weather satellite, Meteosat, is that it sits above 0° latitude and 0° longitude and sends us a picture every thirty minutes. By joining the snapshots up we have an animation – a movie – of our weather.

'Picture' is not really the right word because at night there is no light. Images are what the radiometers on the satellite sense – images of radiance or heat. At night the infrared images reveal the earth's thermal map. We know that clouds are nearly always colder than the oceans; therefore the cold splodges on our thermal image must be clouds. In this way the weather can be 'seen' at night. However, as we can only see the tops of the clouds, the high ice veil may conceal an awesome storm underneath about to hit Britain. We can't switch to the visible image because it's still dark. So satellites are good – but not that good!

One thing they are particularly good for is television weather forecasts. In almost every case, a processed, enhanced and coloured satellite image can show straight away where it is clear and where there are clouds. There are times however, especially at night, when the fog or cloud is at the same temperature as the underlying surface, so the satellite cannot resolve which is which. Nevertheless 'a picture is worth a thousand words', and in the one or two minutes allowed for a weather presentation it is important that viewers can easily take in the information. If the main points of the weather forecast cannot be recalled after the presentation, then it has failed.

Television weather presentations have come a long way since the first weather chart was shown in Britain in 1936. The first personalised weather forecast by a meteorologist on

Left This satellite shows a honeycombe of open cells of fair weather cumulus moving into Northern Ireland and Scotland. Further south there are streets of shallow cumulus over the warming land of southern Ireland, Wales and England.

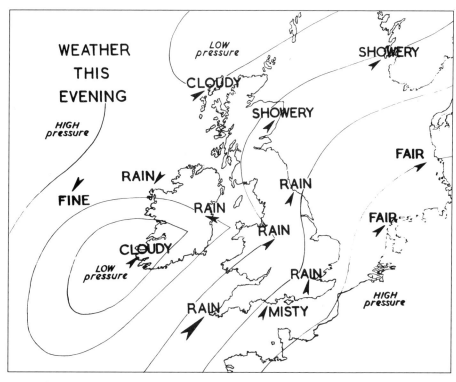

Above One of the first ever weather forecast captions shown on the BBC.

Above George Cowling, the first television weatherman.

television was on the 10th of January 1954. George Cowling was the first television weatherman; he appeared every day at 5 o'clock without fail. He had to travel by tube from the Air Ministry in Kingsway to Shepherd's Bush with his charts tucked under his arm. One day it rained so hard, despite a forecast of a dry day, that he arrived in the television studio with all his charts dripping wet and virtually unusable. For his pains the going rate in those days was ten shillings per appearance, plus the tube fare, on top of his Civil Service salary. The set was an easel and painted background walls, costing fifty pounds. The scripts were written by the Almighty, and He writes them every day. The weatherman would draw isobars on his charts, put the charts on his easel and try to explain the forecast using three different maps headed '3 p.m. Today', 'Tonight' and 'Tomorrow's weather'.

Today the weather forecast has turned into a highly sophisticated and technical presentation. On the early morning television show where I present the weather forecast, I am actually talking about and even pointing to a completely blank wall which is coloured a vivid green. The camera looking at the weatherman and the green wall sends that image to a mixer where everything that is green is replaced by chosen images from another source. It could be a video tape, a graphic or another camera's view. As long as the weatherman is not green, he will remain on the television screen, but instead of the wall the viewer will, for example, see a graphic in the form of a weather chart. Meanwhile in the studio the blank wall is still there, so I have to sneak a look at a television monitor so that I can actually point to the right places. This spectacle certainly fascinates some of the guests on the show. One particular morning David Essex, the singer, asked me: 'Are you really a weatherman or are you just a failed actor?' The advantage of this technique is that the images are as sharp as possible. The weatherman looks slightly awkward, but at least the pictures are clear!

Whatever imagery is used to present the weather forecast on television, meteorologists always go through three basic procedures to arrive at the forecast:

- Analysis: what's going on.
- Forecast distribution of surface atmospheric pressure and fronts.
- Interpretation of the forecast in terms of real weather.

Much of our weather comes from the Atlantic, so analysis is made difficult as nobody lives there. The worldwide network of weather observations is linked together by the global telecommunications system. This provides the basic infrastructure of weather forecasting. Computers all over the world are fed by the data. The forecast charts are a product of the model inside the computer that mimics the atmosphere. People who write numerical models of the atmosphere and program them into the supercomputers of today can take most of the credit for the vast improvement in forecast accuracy over the last decade. Each weather element can be charted for each day ahead, up to ten days. That's not to say the forecast will be correct, but it is a good basis for discussion.

In the end it is the interpretation of all these data streaming out of the computer that is the most important and difficult thing to do. It's all very well having a 'high' over here and a 'low' over there, a 'cold front' here and a 'warm front' there; but how will that affect the weather outside your window? It could be that the forecast chart is right but the actual weather forecast is wrong. The conclusions drawn from the forecast pressure chart could be completely swamped by local effects such as land/sea differences, topography and upper air instability.

Nowadays, most forecasts are quite good. In fact it's now quite surprising when they go wrong. People always seem to remember the times they went wrong and forget the days that went according to plan.

It hasn't been a perfect life, we've had
*   some awkward days,*
The time the vis was 50 yards when we
*   had forecast haze.*
The rain that simply would not stop, the
*   snow that never fell,*
But pass the bottle Jimmy, we have stood
*   our trials well.*

Of course there were some better days,
*   when fronts went through on time,*
When frogs and fosts as prophesied
*   bedecked the land with rime.*
And what we say to all the world is heard
*   and understood,*
So pash the borrel Jimmy, there are times
*   we think we're good.*

Anon.

Above BBC forecasters studying the recordings of a rain gauge on the Air Ministry roof in London, 1954. From left to right, P. McAllen, J. Parry, G. Clifton & D. Dean.

Above John Parry preparing his television weather forecast back in 1954.

Right Nowadays, the electronic mixer shows viewers a multitude of charts in place of the green wall of the studio.

In future years the very short term forecast (nowcast) will be improved by combining satellite movies with a national radar network. Each radar scans its local skies. The strength of the radar echo is a measure of the rainfall that reflected it. A composite map of echoes will show which clouds are actually raining across Britain. Simply extrapolating the movement of the rain clouds will give a very good short term guide as to who can expect rain or snow in the next few hours. To improve the one to five-day ahead forecast, the way forward is to use faster supercomputers with more sophisticated numerical models of the atmosphere. As we saw earlier, for long range forecasts of one week to one month ahead we must accept that errors will cascade through the scales of motion, growing with every time step. This is in accordance with the chaos theory of nature, which says that predictability is simply impossible. This new theory can be demonstrated by starting two almost identical weather systems at the same time and watching what happens. For a short while the two systems go along together, but then some subtle differences begin to appear and grow. Before you know what's going on, the systems have transformed themselves into unbelievably different formations.

Perhaps it will be possible to run several computers each with slightly different initial values to see how long it is before the different forecasts really start to tear away from each other. That might give a good guide as to the degree of confidence to be expected from the long range forecast. Usually with long range forecasts the detail is not attempted; neither is it really expected. Although it ought to be impossible to forecast for months, seasons and years ahead, who knows? If the past is anything to go by – the sky's the limit!

A LOOK AT WEATHER LORE

There is really no such thing as bad weather, only different kinds of good weather.

Quoted by Lord Avebury

Primitive Britons living close to nature must have been acutely aware of and sensitive to the weather. Their keen instincts were no doubt passed on through generations as communities started up and civilisation progressed. As is only to be expected, there is now a veritable hoard of beliefs, proverbs, maxims and sayings concerning the weather. If only this weather lore could be relied on, weather forecasting would be so much easier.

Most people would be pleased if weather lore could simply tell them if it was going to rain or not, so they could make their plans with confidence. If every time it was going to rain, the cows actually laid down – well, that would be something! Surely a cow lies down when it is tired, or maybe when it is chewing cud. The trouble with weather lore is that it relates one observation to one weather event, and says that it will be like that for evermore. Weather lore is a

record of what has happened in the past, and therefore shows the balance of probabilities as to what might very well happen in the future.

The saying goes that if it rains on St Swithin's Day, then it will rain for the next forty days. Well, I am pretty confident that it has never rained for forty days anywhere ever in Britain. It is quite likely that if it rains on St Swithin's Day then it will rain the following day. Even if two things are highly correlated – rain and St Swithin's Day, or rain and cows – there may still be a third factor that is in fact responsible for the apparent relationship between those two things. This implies that weather lore is fundamentally flawed.

St Swithin's Day (15th July) undoubtedly commemorates a famous weather event, and indeed a legend. St Swithin became Bishop of Winchester in 852. When he died in 862 he was buried, at his own request, in an open grave, a

Right A little indecision here! Some cows think its going to rain – or are they just tired?

'vile and unworthy place', where the 'sweet rain of heaven may fall' – not to mention bird droppings. On 15th July 971 it was decided that his remains should be moved inside the church, to a place more fitting for such a holy man; besides which the local smith had reported seeing St Swithin three times in his dreams. It is alleged that St Swithin's spirit was so outraged at being moved that it made the rain fall for forty days, thus delaying the reburial. Ever since then, Britons have cast anxious eyes heavenwards on 15th July – just in case:

> *Oh St Swithin's if thou be fair*
> *For forty days shall rain nae mair,*
> *Oh St Swithin's if thou be wet*
> *For forty days it raineth yet.*

Below St Swithin, the legend says that if it rains on 15th July then it shall rain for the next forty days.

Weather Lore

"The hollow winds begin to blow,
The clouds look black, the glass is low,
The soot falls down, the spaniels sleep,
And spiders from their cobwebs peep.
Last night the sun went pale to bed,
The moon in halos hid her head.
The boding shepherd heaves a sigh,
For, see! a rainbow spans the sky.
The walls are damp, the ditches smell,
Closed is the pink-eyed pimpernel.
Hark! how the chairs and tables crack,
Old Betty's joints are on the rack;
Her corns with shooting pains
   torment her
And to her bed untimely send her.
Loud quack the ducks, the peacocks cry,
The distant hills are looking nigh.
How restless are the snorting swine!
The busy flies disturb the kine,
Low o'er the grass the swallow wings,
The cricket, too, how sharp he sings!
Puss on the hearth, with velvet paws
Sits wiping o'er her whiskered jaws.
Through the clear stream the fishes rise
And nimbly catch th' incautious flies,
The glow-worms, numerous and bright,
Illumed the dewy dell last night.
At dusk the squalid toad was seen
Hopping and crawling o'er the green.
The whirling dust the wind obeys,
And in the rapid eddy plays.
The frog has changed his yellow vest
And in a russet coat is dressed,
Though June, the air is cold and still,
The mellow blackbird's voice is shrill.
My dog, so altered is his taste,
Quits mutton bones on grass to feast.
And, see yon rooks, how odd their flight,
They imitate the gliding kite,
And seem precipitate to fall,
As if they felt the piercing ball –
'Twill surely rain – I see with sorrow
Our jaunt must be put off to-morrow."

Erasmus Darwin (1731-1802)
but also attributed to Edward Jenner

STRICTLY·PROFESSIONAL.

Romantic Amelia (wedded to the young Doctor, Celadon). "LOOK, CELADON—SUCH A BEAUTIFUL SUNSET! THE SKY IS ALL CRIMSON!"
Unromantic Celadon. "YA-AS—APPEARS TO HAVE HAD A MUSTARD PLASTER ON!"

The most spectacular colour scenes are found at sunrise (*below*) and sunset (*right*).

I am sure weather lore has been with us for ever. Although I am fairly cynical about most weather lore, I do believe that some sayings can be proved factually, and it is these lores that I have selected. The first recorded weather dictum can be found in the Bible: 'When it is evening, ye say, it will be fair weather, for the sky is red. And in the morning, it will be foul weather today, for the sky is red and lowering' (Matthew 16: 2–3). The modern version is:

Red sky at night, shepherd's delight,
Red sky in the morning, shepherd's warning.

Most of the large air masses that pass over Britain move from west to east; providing this is the case, the 'red sky' maxim is usually correct. The red in the sky is telling us that the air is fine and dry. Only in dry weather are there particles in the air of the right size to scatter away the blue part of the sun's white rays, thus allowing through the longest waves – the red light. At sunset, in the evening, the dry weather is to come; at sunrise, in the morning, the dry weather must have passed.

Another very good weather aphorism is:

Be it dry or be it wet,
The weather'll always pay its debt.

On average the annual variation in rainfall in Britain is about plus or minus 15 per cent – not much. In 1976, the year of the drought, the following autumn, winter and spring were exceptionally wet. During the drought a water authority installed pumps to make a large river flow backwards. As soon as the pumps had been paid for, the rains came back. In the short term this particular saying is quite likely to be wrong.

A good short term forecast saying is:

Rain before seven, fine before eleven.

Rain bands are typically one hundred miles across and usually move at around thirty miles per hour; therefore frontal rain is usually over in three to four hours. Equally as useful for short term forecasting is:

Ring around the moon, rain is coming soon.

The reflected sunlight from the moon passed through high, wispy ice clouds gives the effect of a halo around the moon by bending the light. When a storm is coming the high ice clouds will thicken with more ice crystals to bend the light. So a persistent and brightened halo will be seen. The brighter the halo, the nearer the storm. On two out of three occasions, rain will follow within ten to twenty hours of a halo.

Again at night, another good forecasting tag is:

Clear moon, frost soon.

A cloudless night allows maximum night-time cooling of the earth, which might, depending on the time of year, lead to frost.

Some people can actually smell the arrival of rain:

When the ditch and pond offend the nose,
Then look for rain and stormy blows.

Although this saying sounds rather ridiculous, though indeed, quaint, there is in fact some truth in it. The atmospheric pressure falls when

Below Ponds can start to smell as rain approaches; so smelling the rain is entirely possible.

rain approaches, which allows fungal growth to increase. Spores are released from ditches and, instead of being contained close to the ground, spread over a wide area. Their odour is earthy, cinnamony and camphoric, and people with a good sense of smell may be able to detect them.

Another sense that is said to detect the rain is hearing:

When the forest murmurs and the mountain roars,
Then close your windows and shut your doors.

As rain approaches, the lower levels of air can be much more uniform and still than on a day of broken cloud cover. The lack of convective turbulence in the air allows sound to travel far and wide. As the storm comes much closer, the roar of the wind drowns out all other noise.

Above This ominous bank of rain cloud dramatically swept in over north London, the streets darkened and the rain came tumbling down.

We all see and enjoy rainbows. Many songs, poems and sayings have been devised to describe our adoration of this beautiful sight. However, some people, as well as treating the rainbow as an object of beauty, actually use it to forecast the weather:

Rainbow in the morning, gives you fair warning.

As mentioned earlier, most of our weather moves from west to east; providing that is the case, this saying is correct. In order to see a rainbow the sun must be on your back. If you see a rainbow in the morning, then a shower in the west is probably approaching. On the other hand, a rainbow in the evening means that the rain has passed and the bad weather will continue to move away to the east:

A rainbow at night be a shepherd's delight.

Another adage that sounds as if it has come straight from *Winnie-the-Pooh* is:

When stars begin to huddle, the earth will soon become a puddle.

This saying is really quite useful. As rain approaches so the clouds increase; this means that sometimes whole areas of stars are covered up by clouds. Where there is a hole in the cloud cover, a little group of stars can be seen huddled together.

The stars have always fascinated mankind. Yet our most famous reference to stars is not an ancient proverb but a nineteenth-century nursery rhyme:

Twinkle, twinkle, little star,
How I wonder what you are!
Up above the world so high,
Like a diamond in the sky!

The twinkling of the stars is caused by all sorts of atmospheric conditions, but alas, is no guide to the weather.

Changes of the moon have always been thought to be connected with weather changes. This probably came about because the phases of the moon are correlated with the tides. However, I can find absolutely no evidence for a connection between the weather and the moon. One theory is that the rain falls more heavily after a new moon. Many researchers have

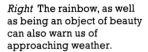

Right The rainbow, as well as being an object of beauty can also warn us of approaching weather.

looked into this but sadly, have come up with no answers. The most accurate rhyme about the moon and the weather is this:

The moon and the weather
May change together
But a change in the moon
Does not change the weather
If we'd no moon at all
(and that may seem strange)
We still should have weather
That's subject to change.

Dew also has its place in weather tradition:

When dew is on the grass, rain will never come to pass.

After a clear and calm night, dew will form on the ground. The air has cooled so much during the night that it has fallen to its dew point temperature.

Dew in the night, next day will be bright.

Assuming the wind stays calm or light, then the fine weather of the morning will stay for the day.

A good forecasting maxim on a cloudy day is:

A patch of blue sky in the morning, big enough to make a Scotsman a pair of trousers, means a fine day.

When a rainy depression is overhead, any break in the low cloud will reveal the high level cloud. But when the depression starts to move away, the high level clouds will have been blown away by the stronger winds found at higher altitudes. So any breaks in the low cloud

Above The expression 'raining cats and dogs' originates from Northern mythology. Odin, the storm god had two attendants, one cat and one dog. The cat symbolises pouring rain and the dog, strong winds.

During the winter months, a snap of Siberian weather can turn up if the wind comes off the frozen Continent. It is the sort of wind that seems to blow straight through you, rather than go around – sometimes called the 'lazy wind':

Point your warm bits to the west
And hope for the best.

An easterly wind is not usually so mobile as a westerly. Therefore if a rain or snow band should turn up from the east, the likelihood is that it may be persistent.

As well as knowing a few weather rhymes for forecasting, it is tremendously helpful to be able to read the face of the sky.

will reveal bright blue sky. From that point on the weather, and hopefully your day, will improve.

On some days the clouds look just like cauliflowers:

When clouds appear like rocks and
towers
The earth's refreshed by frequent
showers.

We've all seen those classic shaped clouds – the ones that look like individual handfuls of cotton wool. These deep bubbly clouds are the rain producing type.

A sunshiny shower, won't last half an hour.

These clouds are created by thermals. As the land heats up during the morning, warm air currents are created; as heat rises, so do these currents. There has to be some compensatory downward motion of air, otherwise all the air would rise and there would be none left below. It is above these downward motions of air that the clear areas are formed, allowing the bright sunshine to beam through. A shower cloud is typically ten miles across and moves at twenty to thirty miles per hour.

Wind direction is an important indicator as to what the weather may be like:

When the wind is from the east
'Tis neither good for man nor beast.

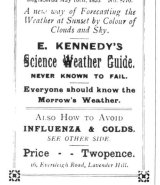

Left Weather lore of 1893 did not come cheap. The pamphlets of the day made some remarkable claims.

Left Cumulus turrets and towers splaying the sunshine across the sky.

1

3

7

4

2

9

The sequence of
approaching rain.

1. Cirrus
2. Cirrocumulus
3. Cirrostratus
4. Altocumulus
5. Altostratus
6. Nimbostratus
7. Stratocumulus
8. Line of stratus in the
   distance with cirro-
   cumulus at high levels.
9. Cumulus
10. Cumulonimbus

5

6

8

10

The clues in the sky are visible, audible and tangible and are all direct expressions of the developing weather. The atmosphere knows what it is going to do next, but can we use the clues to anticipate it?

If it rains while the sun is shining,
The Devil is beating his wife.

This may or may not be true, but at least we can rest assured that the shower won't last long.

Another good indicator is that:

A dappled sky, like a painted woman,
Soon changes its face.

A dappled sky tells us that a change in the weather is on the way. Similarly, it is usually correct to say:

Mackerel sky, mackerel sky,
Never long wet and never long dry.

High altitude fleecy clouds are called cirrocumulus. They have a silky sheen that resembles the arrangement of scales on the back of a mackerel.

Towards the onset of moderate continuous rain there occurs a classic cloud sequence. It starts off with cirrus, the highest wispy curls. Then comes cirrocumulus with its mackerel sky. Cirrostratus follows with a thin milky veil, producing a brightening halo around the sun. The next stage is altocumulus; coarse, fleecy and often in rows. When this gets mixed up with altostratus, a light grey veil is formed which weakens the sunshine.

The day darkens as nimbostratus brings the rain; a heavy veil blocks out the sun. Underneath the solid cloud, patches of grey stratus can be seen scudding across the hills. Eventually the clouds lift and the rain dies out. The normal pattern is for a blanket of stratocumulus, with its gentle undulations, eventually to break up into pancake shapes, allowing the sun to peep through. As the weather improves and more sunshine beams through, the clouds grow taller and become cumulus – the white fluffy clouds. The sun beats down and warms up the land. The cumulus clouds rise with the thermals until eventually they form the biggest cloud of all: cumulonimbus, able to block out the sun completely. It can send rain or hail along with flashes of lightning and blasts of thunder. On the horizon a cumulonimbus can be recognised by its distinctive anvil shaped top.

The weather, having tens of elements, hundreds of feedbacks and therefore thousands of possibilities, does not always follow the classic path. Sometimes it gets interfered with and ends up doing something totally different. So each day must be taken on its merits and viewed afresh.

What is this life if, full of care,
We have no time to stand and stare?
No time to stand beneath the boughs
And stare as long as sheep or cows.
     W. H. Davies, *Leisure* (1911)

When in fair weather the cumulus start growing and the tops of the clouds exhibit a brilliant white, then those tops are icing up, ready to make rain. When the cumulus clouds are spread out under a stable layer of air they become stratocumulus – pancake shaped clouds. This is a sign that the sinking high altitude air is winning and fine weather is settling in.

Aeroplanes in the sky often leave trails of condensation; these are called contrails. They can be seen across the highest level of the weather sphere. The vapour trail freezes before it has time to evaporate. If the high level air becomes moist then the contrails will persist for hours. This could be a clear indication of a change in the weather.

More help in forecasting the weather can come from observing the behaviour of various plants and animals. After all, the most famous image of a weather prophet is someone

Right Contrails left by planes can be an indication of a change in the weather.

examining a pine cone or a cluster of seaweed. Some plants can tell us roughly how much water is in the air given the temperature and pressure – the relative humidity. Seaweed contains magnesium chloride, which is hydroscopic: it absorbs invisible water molecules from the air. As rain approaches the relative humidity rises, so the seaweed feels damp to humans. Believe it or not, a human is also a good indicator of rising relative humidity. As the humidity rises, hair gets shorter. Human hair can actually be used to move a pointer or swing out the man in a Dutch weatherhouse.

It has often been said that the scarlet pimpernel is a poor man's weatherglass:

Now look! Our weatherglass is spread –
The Pimpernel, whose flower
Closes its leaves and spotted red
Against a rainy hour.

The flower closes its leaves when the relative humidity rises to about 80 per cent. This is quite a reasonable sign that rain is coming, and since the plant grows in British hedgerows it's pretty cheap.

Leaves are again very cheap:

When the leaves show their undersides
Be very certain that rain betides.

Increasingly damp air softens leaf stalks, which bend and expose the undersides of the leaves. In contrast the dandelion will only release its seeds if the air is dry. How many of us have picked a dandelion and puffed away a thousand seeds? If the air is dry they will float for miles; if the air is heavy and damp then the seeds will just drop, meaning rain is on the way.

Left The scarlet pimpernel, blooming with weather lore history.

Left I think the dandelion makes a pretty useless clock, but it has been known to be a useful rain forecaster.

Right Migrating birds often fly in a **V** formation so that the followers can take advantage of the lift provided by the wing vortices of the leaders.

Right A high flying swallow on a dry day carrying food to its young.

Every year the big question is: has winter finally finished, and is spring here to stay?

Button to chin, till May be in.
Cast not a clout, till May be out.

This doggerel refers to either May the month, or the may flower of the hawthorn tree. The flower is usually out before the month is over, so I think the first part of the rhyme refers to the month and the second to the flower. So when you see the hawthorn flowering, it's time to put away your winter clothes.

Animals display many peculiar reactions to changes in atmospheric conditions, but whether they actually foretell the weather is open to discussion. Birds seem to play an important part in weather lore. It's not surprising really, considering the thousands of migratory miles that birds have to travel. If they can foretell the immediate weather forecast, then their passage will be much easier.

Cockerels scraping the ground contentedly are said to be a sign of good settled weather, but that's not a forecast. Rooks, on the other hand, are said to foretell rough weather. If they twist and tumble in flight on leaving the rookery, then rain is said to follow.

Swallows high, staying dry;
Swallows low, wet 'till blow.

There is a lot of sense and logic to this rhyme and it applies to any high flying, insect eating bird. During fine settled weather, when the sun is shining and the sky is blue, insects are plentiful and tend to rise high in the sky. Insects are the swallow's staple diet, so where the insects go so does the swallow. If the air is heavy with rain and the wind is starting to blow, then the swallow will stay close to the ground as the insects won't be flying very high.

*Wild geese, wild geese, ganging to the
  sea,
Good weather it will be;
Wild geese, wild geese, ganging to the
  hill,
The weather it will spill.*

Again this rhyme would appear to make sense. If there is going to be a storm, the worst place to be would be the sea. There again, if it was a hot, sunny afternoon, a short spell on the sea would be lovely. Geese are said also to forecast storms by cackling more than usual and fighting for their food.

The swan is said to be an excellent forecaster of floods: *'There is no doubt that they have an instinctive prescience of floods, for it is a well-known fact that before heavy rains the birds whose home is on the banks of the Thames raise their nests so as to save their eggs from being chilled by the water'* (C. Swainson). Whether any other birds do this, I don't know; it does seem to be a good self-preservation feature that a wild bird would need to have for survival. Again: *'If the swan flies against the wind, it is a certain indication of a hurricane within twenty-four hours, generally within twelve'* (correspondent in *The Athenaeum*). Maybe we should all have been watching the swans back in October 1987!

Left These elegant and intelligent birds raise the level of their riverside nests if they think a flood is imminent.

The kingfisher has much weather lore history. Another name for the kingfisher is halcyon, which in Greek means 'conceiving on the sea'. It used to be thought that the birds laid eggs at sea in floating nests of fishbone. According to Greek legend, Halcyone, daughter of the God of Winds, married Ceyx, son of the Day Star. Ceyx drowned in a storm at sea. The gods took pity on his wife and restored him to life; however, they turned them both into kingfishers. For two weeks each year, while Halcyone is on her nest, her father holds back the wind – hence the expression 'halcyon days'.

It is thought that the hedgehog has strange long range forecasting abilities. When it awakes from the winter hibernation period it checks whether its shadow can be seen in daylight. If the shadow can be seen, then the hedgehog disappears again for a week or so, presumably because clear skies mean a high risk of night frosts. Moles are also thought to be weather forecasters. Country people say that large and numerous mole hills foretell warm wet weather. Maybe that theory could be connected to the behaviour patterns of the earthworm, the mole's favourite food.

Top Right Another name for the kingfisher is halcyon, the expression 'Halcyon days' comes from the kingfisher's weather lore history.

Right The reappearance of the hedgehog after its hibernation has always been taken as a sign that winter is finally over.

Given the fact that animals live much closer to nature than we do, I believe them to be by and large poor weather forecasters. There are thousands of sayings concerning how animals foretell the weather, some of which I think are very dubious. However, I will say that they may have more basis in fact than the old wives' tales.

Spiders work hard and spin their webs a little before wind, as if desiring to anticipate it, for they cannot spin when the wind begins to blow.
Bacon

Where to Live in the Future Climate

If you can look into the seeds of time,
And say which grain will grow and which will not,
Speak then to me, who neither beg nor fear
Your favours nor your hate.

William Shakespeare, *Macbeth*

UNSEASONABLE SEASONING.

Summer (*to* Spring). "YOU WINTER'D 'EM!—I'VE WATER'D 'EM! LET'S HOPE THEY'VE LIKED IT!!!"

The very best climate to live in is of course happiness. Choosing the right place to live can go a long way to achieving that goal. Not many of us can choose to live anywhere we please, but it is still worth knowing how the weather affects where we live. This can be of considerable practical use the next time you want to move house.

Living in built-up areas, with all that congestion and noise, at first glance seems a way to avoid the weather. In the city the course of nature around the seasons is hardly noticeable. However, in cities the height and closeness of the buildings can prove to be very claustrophobic. Time spent in another building's shadow can cast an unnatural gloom over a home. In Britain the winds are usually from the south-west; therefore it's a good idea to avoid living directly downwind of a smelly factory. The west of a town usually has the freshest air, due to the prevailing winds, although hilltops will nearly always be fresh.

During the cold clear nights of winter, the temperature in the city may be 8°C warmer than the surrounding rural areas. The city is like a giant night storage heater, releasing the heat of the masonry slowly into the chill of the night. In daytime the winter temperature difference is less but still significant. In summer the city becomes an island of warmth; an immense amount of heat can be thrown up over the concrete, sometimes resulting in cloudbursts that can flood places downwind. A good example was the Hampstead storm of 14th August 1975. The heavens opened, creating probably the largest cloudburst to occur in Britain this century.

Whatever the season, the streets that run north-south will be warmer and sunnier than the shady east-west streets. Flats with large windows or lots of glass may look good, but it is an exhausting task trying to control the temperature, especially during hot sunny days and on dark winter nights with a strong chilly wind. It is worth remembering that those streets shut in amongst high buildings may see no sun at all.

The long straight city streets can funnel the wind and strengthen it. As the sun heats up the pavements, thermal currents are created; the winds in city streets can therefore be very gusty. It is not unusual to find a gale blowing at

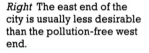
Right The east end of the city is usually less desirable than the pollution-free west end.

Far Left Vast areas of glass used in office blocks create unbearably hot microclimates.

Left The Hampstead storm, 1975. The highest point in London – Hampstead and Highgate suffered badly from the biggest point rainfall ever recorded in Britain.

Above Will the rising sea levels combined with the high tide and storm surge eventually over-power the Thames barrier and flood these buildings?

one corner, with rubbish being swept upwards in a whirlwind, while just a few hundred yards away in a park the wind is almost calm. Living near crossroads means the wind will be three times stronger than normal, as at the crossroads all the funnelled winds meet. Winds can also be funnelled by river embankments and swirl into turbulence over riverside homes.

More importantly, riverside homes and dockland developments in the towns will be threatened by rising sea levels in the new enhanced greenhouse world. The increasing risk from flooding will no doubt be reflected in the cost of house insurance. It might be a good idea to ask around in the local area to find

out if the river or sea has ever come close to flooding before, and then estimate what an extra 60 centimetres added to the water level might do to the surrounding area.

In contrast to the cities, the remote unspoilt parts of Britain might very well appeal. Certainly to be able to watch and enjoy nature and the elements through all the seasons might be worth it for its own sake. However, today for such areas there is a new and menacing threat, probably the most serious local weather problem in northern Europe: acid rain. Unfortunately it tends usually to affect the remotest parts of Britain, which until now have been least spoilt by man. Remote areas are most sensitive to acid rain because typically they have thin soils on hard granite rocks, which tend to be low on alkaline elements, especially calcium and magnesium. Large areas of Britain's uplands have soil, rocks and lakes which cannot resist acidification. While emissions of greenhouse gases are probably changing the world's climate, the related emissions of sulphur dioxide and nitrous oxides from power stations, industrial plants and motor vehicles are changing the microclimates of soils and lakes in remote parts of Britain. Aquatic life in these regions faces a very uncertain future; already a considerable amount of life in the Scandinavian lakes has been killed off, and it could be that Britain will follow suit. What may save the day for remote areas is that they are a long way from the sources of pollution, and with any luck most of it will continue to fall outside Britain as it is carried away on the prevailing south-westerlies.

From vast industrial areas and coal fuelled power stations, pollutants are spread out along the direction of the wind. Much of the acid rain is dry invisible rain and falls out as gases or particles close to the source. At the very least this is not good for the soil. So anyone keen on gardening should avoid living near coal fired power stations. During their travels the pollutants react with oxidising gases in the air and

Above British trees are, as yet, not this bad but in other parts of Europe, acid rains and mists are killing off the trees.

Right Nelson's column, made from Portland stone, gets a face lift after years of neglect in London smogs.

change into sulphuric and nitric acids of low volatility, which are then captured by cloud drops and fall as rain: hence the name 'acid rain'. However, 'dry' acid rain is still important because, believe it or not, cloud and rain are around for only a small fraction of time. The rate at which acids are made in the sky depends upon the time of year; sunlight is needed, and therefore the most acid is formed in high summer. So anyone looking for a home with endless trouble-free salmon and trout fishing through the summer might do well to note that salmon and trout are especially vulnerable to acid levels. If the streams, rivers and lakes have a measured pH level less than 4.5 the fish will die. The pH numbers indicate the strength of the acid: they range from pH 1 (strongly acid) to pH 6 (weakly acid), and then from pH 8 (weakly alkaline) to pH 14 (strongly alkaline).

Unpolluted rain and snow almost everywhere in the world are naturally slightly acid, with pH values around 5. The oceans are the major source of sulphur compounds; these escape through sea spray, which makes the rain slightly acid. Consequently soils have to cope with a little bit of acid all the time. Most resistant of all are the North and South Downs of southern England, where the soil is rich in the alkaline calcium that will neutralise any acid rain that falls on it. Anyone keen to avoid acid soils would do well to consider Kent, Sussex, Hampshire and Surrey for their gardens.

Left Even the Magnesian Limestone of the York Minster is attacked by acid rain.

Left Man-made river pollution on top of increasing acidity can kill fish and river life.

free period may expand. Dark soils absorb the most heat during the day and are the least susceptible to frost. At the extreme, black tarmac will often reach around 40°C when the shade air temperature is around 20°C. Having a layer of clay can cause major problems during prolonged drought (and these may become more frequent in our enhanced greenhouse world). The clay will eventually dry out, and at the same time will shrink and move. This can play havoc with the foundations of a house.

A house next to a wood has a special microclimate. In the summer, if the trees cast their shadows over the house in the early morning or late afternoon it can be remarkably cold. However, on cold clear nights the wood can protect the house from the extreme cold by reducing heat loss from the house or by giving up its own warm air. During the day a dense evergreen wood is a dark, cool, dank place with next to no weather inside. Woods further uphill from a house can be a useful barrier, guiding the colder denser pools of night air around the house and down the hill.

If you cycled cross-country at night over hills, down dips, through woods and along open flat land, you would notice how quickly winds and temperatures can change. On average the higher you go, the lower the temperature. Ben Nevis, which is 1300 metres high, is so cold at the summit that it has no growing season and is often capped with snow. Also, on average the wind increases with elevation, so that hilltops are usually breezy places. One disadvantage of living on a hilltop is that the cloud base can lower and shroud the home in a chilly grey damp surround. Roads to a hillside house can soon become blocked by drifting snow in the

Above Woods on a hillside can act as cold air blocks at night to protect the house from extremes of cold.

Below Dark soils heat up more than light soils and are less prone to night frosts.

Below Right Hilltop living can be unusually damp when the cloud base lowers.

Soil in general can be a big factor in choosing a place to live. Sandy soils are more absorbent of heat and therefore dry out more quickly. So on clear nights, for example, the temperature over sandy soils can fall 4 or 5°C more than elsewhere. In winter this means more frosts, so over the year the growing season may be cut back an extra two months. Damaging frosts over sandy flatlands may occur at any time of the year, apart from late June to late August. In a new greenhouse world, this frost-

winter. Even on a summer's day the wind strength outside a hillside house can spoil any thoughts of sitting in the sun. At night the wind moaning around the house can have an unsettling effect. On the other hand the sharp and colourful views from a good vantage point on clear days can make it all worthwhile.

Not all hillside homes are exposed to the wind, but those that are, and all other homes on very exposed sights can expect a lot of trouble from driving rain. Heavy rain falling at an angle has a remarkable ability to seek out and find all the cracks on the outside of the house and penetrate to the inside. This adds to the moisture created by the inhabitants. Exposure to the wind increases the rate of heat loss from the structure, making internal condensation and accompanying moulds more likely. Exposure also affects the look of the surrounding countryside. Even the warmest parts of Scotland cannot sustain tree growth as the land is too exposed to strong winds. However, on a warm summer's day the wild, windswept, treeless landscape of the Scottish Highlands is, to my mind, one of the finest sights in the world.

Above The slope and direction of the hill are important to know when working out how to get the most sunshine.

Left The open, exposed highlands offer little or no shelter to crofters.

Of all the weather elements to consider when choosing a house location, probably the most important is sunshine. The sun may not climb high enough in the sky to overcome the shadow of a hill. So hills that slope upwards towards the south can be rather dark, depressing places during winter. The sun at midwinter climbs to about 10° elevation above the horizon. By the equinoxes in March and September the sun will reach 35° elevation. At midsummer the sun will almost reach 60° – a little less in northern parts of Britain, a little more in the south. In May, probably the best weather month in Britain, the sun rises to about 45° elevation.

During May the seas that surround Britain are still at their coldest, and so by and large May can be one of the sunniest months with the least cloud. It's also the time of birdsong, and gardens are ablaze with colour. It is a favourite time of the year for sitting outside and enjoying the evenings. So it is very important to make sure that the westerly aspect has no major obstruction to block out the sun. From our climate records it would seem that the best places to live for the longest summery conditions are Cork, south Devon, Dorset, Sussex and the Channel Islands. The Continental summers that sometimes visit the south-east of Britain rarely reach the northernmost parts. However, it's interesting to note that, in Shetland and northern Scotland, midsummer's day is so long that it is quite possible to read out in the open at midnight. So midsummer is something rather special in northern Britain. Continental summers are most likely to turn up over the south-east quarter of England (nearest the Continent). The region has a wide variety of land, ranging from limestone and chalk to sand and some clay. The driest sites will be the ridges of chalk, and the dampest sites will be the valleys of clay.

The most constant type of climate – relatively frost free and fairly mild – is to be found in Cornwall, Wales, the Western Isles of Scotland and the west of Ireland. The Gulf Stream has a marked effect on the climate in these areas and keeps even the winters fairly mild.

A seaside home will usually have a very special microclimate. However, there is now the increasing threat that rising sea levels may one day flood low lying coastal areas and erode the coastal strip. A lot will depend on how well sea defences are made. The most striking feature of the microclimate of seasides is the summer sea-breeze. A gentle breeze brings pleasant relief from the heat of the afternoon. However, sea-breezes can become irritating; being sand-blasted on a beach is not nice.

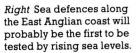

Right Sea defences along the East Anglian coast will probably be the first to be tested by rising sea levels.

Left Houses too close to the sea are vulnerable to coastal erosion.

When the sea is colder than some of the warm air masses that roll over it, the air is cooled to condensation temperature, producing extensive sea fogs which are then brought in by the light breeze. In Devon and Cornwall the sea fogs are called sea *frets*. *Mizzle* is another term – a combination of mist and drizzle. On the east coast of Scotland the sea fog and seemingly endless grey cover is called *haar*. It makes for damp *driecht* depressing days. Even in summer, sea fogs can roll inland. During the night the fog may roll far inland, and then by day the sun will slowly burn it back to the coast.

Sometimes it's touch and go as to whether it will clear up on the coast. There can be a strange grey world right on the coast, whereas just a fraction of a mile inland there is blazing sunshine.

So all in all there are a surprising number of microclimates across the British Isles to choose from when deciding where to live. Luckily we are all different, so it's unlikely that we will all go rushing off to the same area. The longer we live in one place, the more acclimatised we become and the more we resist changing. But for some, a change of weather and climate brought on by a move is greatly beneficial.

Below Coastal areas can sometimes be shrouded in grey foggy worlds even when there is bright sunshine a few miles inland.

THE FUTURE CLIMATE OF BRITAIN

Is there in the world a climate more uncertain than our own? And, which is a natural consequence, is there anywhere a people more unsteady, more apt to discontent?

William Congreve *Amendments of Mr Collier's False and Imperfect Citations*

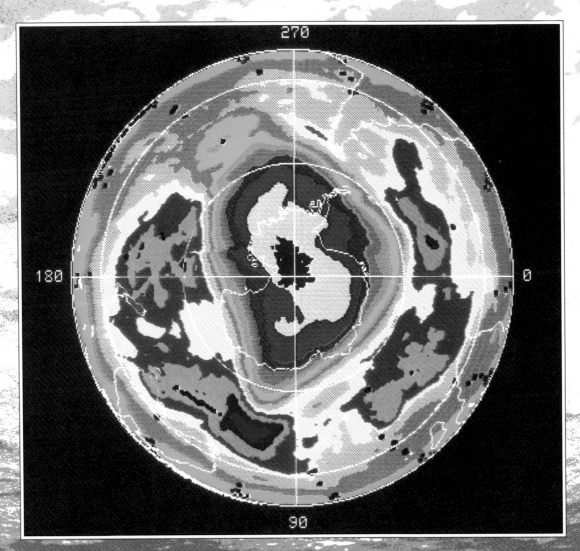

Weather is a snapshot of the atmosphere in constant turbulent motion. Climate, on the other hand is like the plot of a film that could be made by joining millions of snapshot frames in sequence and replaying them at the usual twenty-four frames per second. Climate is the average of all weather events over a wide area and a very long time.

Now surely climate cannot be predicted; after all, sometimes we can't even predict tomorrow's weather, so how can we predict the future of our climate for the years to come. Well, weather and climate are very different. Weather is deterministic; that is to say what the weather *will* do depends on what the weather *is* doing. So any tiny errors in the analysis of what the weather is doing (and there are always plenty) will, as the forecast is worked out, cascade through the scales of motion in the atmosphere to make the errors grow and grow. The further ahead the forecast tries to go, the more the errors grow. The predictability limit is about ten days. By contrast, the climate is more predictable – in a certain way.

A good analogy is a game of pinball. Typically the ball strikes pin after pin in a totally random and virtually unpredictable way. A small spec of dust along the path of the ball or an unexpected vibration in the room can send the ball to the next pin at a slightly different angle than expected. As a consequence the error then grows and grows. If we had the patience to watch a thousand balls it might be possible to work out the likelihood of any one pin on the board being hit in the future. A difference would be noticed if say a very large ball was used and only the first pin was hit, or if an extremely powerful striker was used and all the pins were hit. Most importantly, if we upset the balance of things, say by adding more slant to the table, we should then be able to come to some conclusions about how it would affect the behaviour of the balls. In this analogy the weather is the detailed path of the individual balls and the climate is the average of those paths. Therefore although the exact weather cannot be predicted with certainty (except in special cases), the climate generally can. In particular if we upset

Right The burning of coal, oil and gas for energy releases five to six thousand million tonnes of carbon into the air every year. The EEC is responsible for 13 per cent. Carbon dioxide is the most important greenhouse gas because of its vast tonnage emitted.

Previous Page NASA satellite picture of the hole in the ozone layer.

our atmosphere, say by dumping our waste into it, we should still be able to predict the new climate.

The response of the climate to man-made contamination of the atmosphere is very probably the most important environmental issue of our time. The greatest contamination is the giga-tonnes of carbon dioxide (CO_2) released into the atmosphere every year. Carbon dioxide is a colourless, tasteless, non-toxic invisible gas breathed out by animals and absorbed by plants and oceans. Carbon dioxide comes mainly from the burning of fossil fuels such as coal, oil and gas – that have for many millions of years been stored below the earth's surface. To a lesser extent the burning of the rain forests releases additional carbon dioxide into the atmosphere, whereas normally, the rain forests would otherwise take out the carbon dioxide.

As long ago as 1899 the Swedish chemist Svante Arrhenius suggested that changing concentrations of carbon dioxide in the atmosphere could be a major cause of climate change. He recognised that carbon dioxide, along with another gas, had been keeping the earth warm for billions of years. The other gas is water vapour.

Without carbon dioxide and water vapour in our atmosphere, the mean earth temperature would be –18°C instead of our current 15°C. This higher mean temperature occurs because of the greenhouse effect. The 'greenhouse effect' is so called as the effects the earth will suffer are the same as a greenhouse being heated up by the sun. The sun's heat is absorbed and trapped by the glass and there is no way the heat can escape, gradually the greenhouse gets warmer and warmer. In reality the two gases allow solar heating through rather like the greenhouse glass, but they do not allow all the earth's warmth back out to space. These so called 'greenhouse gases' absorb some of the earth's heat, and reradiate it back to earth. The 'greenhouse effect' traps additional heat in the lower atmosphere, which causes global warming of the land, sea, and the lower layers of the atmosphere. Increasing the concentration of greenhouse gases will increase global warming.

In 1957 two scientists, R. Revelle and H. Suess, wrote:

Human beings are now carrying out a large-scale geophysical experiment of the kind that could not have happened in the past or be repeated in the future.

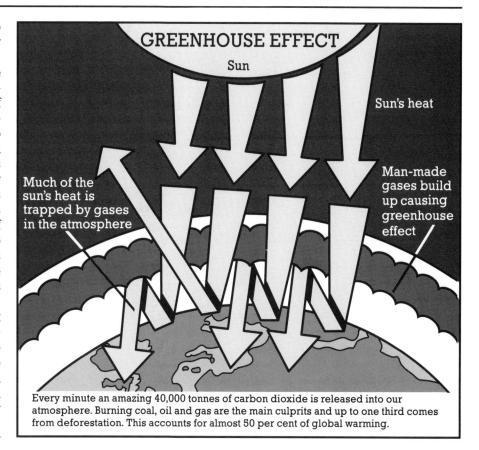

GREENHOUSE EFFECT

Sun

Sun's heat

Much of the sun's heat is trapped by gases in the atmosphere

Man-made gases build up causing greenhouse effect

Every minute an amazing 40,000 tonnes of carbon dioxide is released into our atmosphere. Burning coal, oil and gas are the main culprits and up to one third comes from deforestation. This accounts for almost 50 per cent of global warming.

Within a few centuries, we are returning to the atmosphere and the oceans the concentrated organic compounds stored in the sedimentary rocks over hundreds of millions of years. The experiment, if adequately documented, may yield a far reaching insight into processes determining weather and climate.

In 1988 the British prime minister, Margaret Thatcher, made a speech to the Royal Society, saying: 'But with all these enormous changes happening quickly: increasing population; intensity of agriculture; intense use of fossil fuels; all these concentrated into such a short period of time, we have unwittingly begun a massive experiment with the system of this planet itself.' The prime minister's speech focused political attention on what scientists had been saying for years: if measures are not taken to limit global warming then humankind faces an increasingly difficult future, and some natural ecosystems face no future at all.

The media were quick to follow, and soon captured the new mood of concern in Britain for the environment, which had been building

The destruction of rain forests changes the reflectivity of the land and therefore the amount of solar energy absorbed. As we destroy the lungs of our planet (as plants absorb carbon dioxide from the air) the last habitats of rare and potentially beneficial flora and fauna are rapidly disappearing. As a consequence many endangered species face extinction.

since the birth of the modern environment movement in the late sixties. The great British obsession with the environment began. The year of the green revolution in Britain was 1988–89. The Green Party collected some 2 million votes in the European parliamentary elections. A Mintel poll worked out that 27 per cent of the population would pay 25 per cent more for greener products. Shops were suddenly selling 'environmentally friendly' versions of what they were selling before.

Whatever measures are adopted to curb greenhouse gases, the world is already committed to some global warming, as roughly half the carbon dioxide released since the industrial revolution is still in the atmosphere and the amount is increasing. The pollution is ameliorated by ocean plankton which can absorb carbon dioxide from the air. In fact the oceans soak up a third to a half of the carbon dioxide produced each year. Even so, there has been an observed 25 per cent increase in the amount of

carbon dioxide in the atmosphere worldwide in the last 100 years. This means that if things continue as they have done in the past, and taking into account emissions of other greenhouse gases, then by 2030 the atmosphere will hold effectively double the carbon dioxide levels compared with pre-industrial times. The best estimate of the consequential forced global warming is an average of 2°C – a little less at the equator, and a little more at the poles. It is the degree, and the pace of change that matters. Just a 4°C rise in global temperatures was enough to take Britain out of the last ice age some 10,000 years ago, when ice sheets extended as far south as London and the tarns of Wales.

So far this century the global warming is estimated to be 0.5°C. When compared to other 100 year periods in the past, 0.5°C warming is seen to be statistically significant. The 1980s are known to be globally the warmest decade since records began. The British winter of 1988–89

Below A typical scene during the Industrial Revolution. For thousands of years prior to the revolution the level of greenhouse gases were more or less constant. As the world became industrialised and agriculture developed, so the gases increased.

was one of the warmest on record, and the summer of 1989 was also one of the hottest and driest on record. However satellite measurements, supported by land and sea observations have shown no global warming trend over the 1980s, despite the obvious warmth of the decade in comparison with the last 100 years. This fact highlights the problems scientists have in detecting global warming.

However, all this could simply be natural variability. Sceptics argue that it is too early to tell whether man is overheating the world, and so too early to try expensive remedies. Greenhouse effect experts have been known to get so impatient, so emotional, as if about to throw stones!

The underlying fear that many climatologists have is that global warming will become a fact of life, bringing about climate change that will cause three catastrophies:

● Flooding.

● Crop failure.

● Unprecedented extremes of weather.

Flooding of coastal Britain could happen because global warming causes oceans to expand, and polar ice and mid-latitude glaciers to melt. In the unlikely event of the entire Antarctic ice cap melting over hundreds of years, then The Netherlands and Belgium would disappear. The Atlantic would flood the whole of middle Ireland. London would also go under. However, Antarctica is very likely far too cold for any substantial melting.

The melting of continental ice sheets and the warming seas rising by thermal expansion are likely to raise sea levels some tens of centimetres by 2030. The complicated varying uplift of the earth's mantle following the melting of ice sheets would counteract the rise in sea level a little in some places. In Britain however, a slow downwards tilting from the north-west of Scotland to the south-east of England would add another ten or so centimetres by 2030. This is one of the reasons for building the Thames barrier at Woolwich to protect London. So altogether sea levels around Britain might be expected to rise by as much as 40 centimetres by 2030, assuming global warming of around 2°C.

Of course, confidence in this forecast has to be extremely low, because there are just so many unknowns. In particular, no one knows

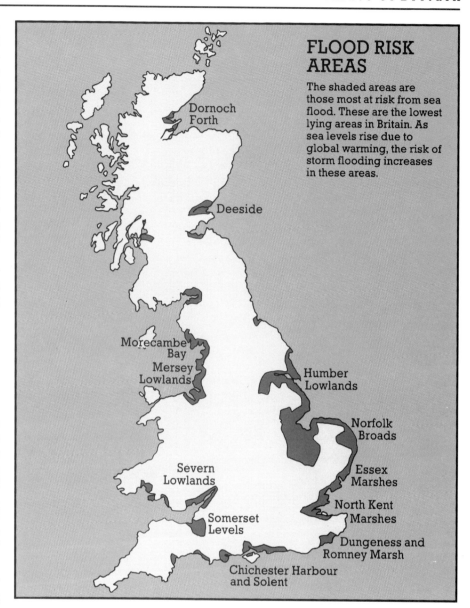

FLOOD RISK AREAS

The shaded areas are those most at risk from sea flood. These are the lowest lying areas in Britain. As sea levels rise due to global warming, the risk of storm flooding increases in these areas.

GLOBAL WARMING THIS CENTURY

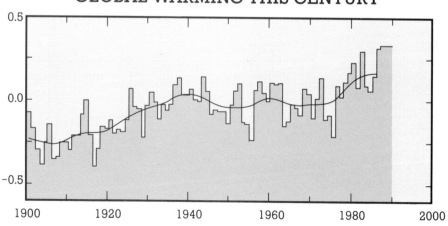

Above This is a satellite image of light reflected by the green pigment in algae. They are abundant in the red areas which are the warm, nutrient rich waters.

Right Algae or plankton living on the surface of the ocean absorb carbon dioxide from the air. Tiny shrimp like animals eat the algae and then drop to deep water and excrete carbon. Millions of tonnes fall to the sea bed – the natural sink for atmospheric carbon dioxide.

Left Icebergs that melt in a warmer world will make no difference to the sea level, just as melting ice cubes in a drink won't give you more drink. However, if ice shelves that are frozen to rock break away, then this would cause sea levels to rise. This is because the ice (water) is falling into the sea, therefore increasing the sea's volume.

Left If sea levels rise the Thames Barrier will become invaluable. When a storm surge coincides with a high tide and heavy rainfall, the barrier gates will lift from their normal horizontal position to their vertical position to stop the sea.

Right Ely Cathedral, situated in the heart of the low-lying Fens. A large proportion of the Fens are below sea level. Fortunately Ely Cathedral was built on high ground, otherwise known as 'The Isle of Ely'.

defences if the expected 2°C warming comes about.

Crop failure will hit some places harder than others. It may be that the crop failures abroad will have a greater impact on Britain than the relatively minor shifts in agriculture expected after a 2°C warming in Britain. For example, the 1988 USA drought may have been a consequence of global warming; no one knows. The drought brought back memories of the 1930s and 1950s 'dustbowl' years when widespread and severe droughts affected the Midwestern states. Any climatic shift that could cause deserts to spread would threaten the 'bread basket' of the world. It's easy to imagine the world's grain reserves becoming exhausted, and famine continuing in third world countries. The political ramifications would affect everyone. However, possibly the 1988 drought was a chance occurrence due to natural year-to-year variations, and might just as well have occurred with a much smaller increase in greenhouse gases, as was the case in the 1930s. It will be very suspicious though if the Midwest USA suffers another drought soon.

how exactly the ice sheets will respond to global warming. However, I would not buy a house in a docklands development, or a house by the seaside! A rise of 40 centimetres is frightening when added to high tide and a storm surge. It's easy to imagine the fens under water and the Isle of Ely an island again. The British Isles will have to invest heavily in sea

Right There can only be a matter of days left for this house as the cliff crumbles beneath. Recent reports suggest that our sea defences should be set back from the sea, therefore abandoning land.

Left & Below Scenes from
the 'dustbowl' of Midwest
America during the 1930's.
Poor weather and intense
farming ruined the land. It
is just possible that in our
enhanced greenhouse
world, endless heat, damp
and severe droughts could
become more common.

Above An English vineyard in Kent. One consolation with global warming is that English wine could look forward to vintage years!

Right It is strange to imagine that the Sahara desert was once a swampy quagmire. In a warmer world will the rains return?

This could be good news for many. Continental style cafés with their tables on the pavements make a pleasant change. The wine makers of southern England could look forward to vintage years. Some crops could even be harvested twice each year in a warmer, longer growing season. New crops could be grown in Scotland, such as french beans, sugar beet and maize.

With a 2°C global warming on its way, the northern boundaries for crops will shift about 300 miles north. Most of upland Britain up to 600 feet should be able to support crops, so sheep and cattle farming may intensify. The extra carbon dioxide in the air will most likely produce a more vigorous growth of crops like wheat, barley and potatoes.

Some areas would suffer though, because hard winters are essential to keep down pests which spread diseases to plants. For example, the seed potato crop from Tayside could easily be wiped out. All in all Britain is probably one of the lucky places in the world, because it is probably wealthy enough to adapt to climate change.

Curiously enough the predicted global warming of 2°C by 2030 would be analogous to going back 6000 years. That was the warmest

In Britain the average day-to-day weather and climate may not change very much with global warming of 2°C. Southernmost counties of England would most likely have a more Mediterranean climate, drier and warmer than it is now. Other parts of Britain would most likely have a warmer and wetter climate than now.

time since the most recent ice age, which was at its height some 18,000 years ago. This type of warm era is known as a 'climatic optimum'. It is thought that deserts were almost absent, and that the Sahara desert was a vast swamp full of crocodiles and hippopotami. However, soils in temperate latitudes were drier, especially across the interior of continents, suggesting the threat of crop failures. Going even further back in time to try and find an analogy, the Pliocene climatic optimum of four million years ago was around 4°C globally warmer than now. This sort of change may, some scientists predict, be with us by 2050 as greenhouse gases go on increasing. In the past the warmer world was also much wetter, and Africa was covered by forests. A warmer wetter world may well benefit Canada and the Soviet Union, but Britain being a relatively small island may still see little change.

Probably the biggest noticeable change in the day-to-day weather across Britain, in response to global warming of around 2°C, will be the rain in winter. It's hard to imagine it could be wetter, but the expected warming demands an average of an extra one millimetre of rain per day during winter. Summer could go either way or stay the same, but the intense rainfall events which often occur in summer are likely to become more intense. The winter of 1989–90 was the wettest on record for the west of Scotland, with some places having rain at some time on every day for three months! People living there may agree that they get so much rain in winter, that a drop more would make no difference. Typically England and Wales over the last twenty years have seen seasonal rainfall vary by 15 per cent either way. With global warming this variation should increase. That is, summers could swing from droughts to floods more often than ever before. The key element appears to be evaporation. Global warming means more evaporation, a moister atmosphere and more rain. If these rains could reach the interiors of vast continents, then that would be a good thing. Most of the time this would be the case for Britain, but for weather that comes from the Continent – dry weather – increased evaporation in summer would lead to large soil moisture deficits or droughts.

Another noticeable change in the weather by 2030 in Britain will be snowfall – or rather lack of it. Already snow in southern England is a rarity that makes front page news. The last white Christmas in London was in 1970. With the expected global warming, snowfall in Scotland may well become a thing of the past. On the

Above 'There's no business like *snow* business'!

Continent, the winters of both 1988–89 and 1989–90 nearly bankrupted the skiing businesses on the Alps and Pyrenees; they were saved only at the last minute by late falls of snow.

Unprecedented extreme weather events like floods, storms, heatwaves and droughts are likely to occur more frequently in an enhanced greenhouse world. The extra greenhouse gases by 2030 will add an extra 4 watts per square metre of heat to the surface of the world. This is extra energy that could allow weather events to become more intense, more extreme. Additionally, extra evaporation will allow more latent heat of condensation (more energy) to be added to storms. It's like having a run of climate over the years with peaks along the way; suddenly the whole run is lifted up a notch so that the new peaks reach even greater heights. It will be perceived as an increase in the incidence of extreme weather events.

The exact future climate of Britain depends on whether the world systems work to amplify or reduce the initial warming. This is a minefield of a subject and still in its infancy. The major problems are:

- Ocean temperature lags behind.
- Ocean currents change direction.
- Clouds block both heating and cooling.
- Ice caps grow with more snowfall.

Above Different levels of cloud contribute to global warming in opposite ways. The low water clouds reflect away sunshine whereas the high ice clouds trap the earth's heat.

from west to east (opposite to normal) along tropical latitudes, usually arriving at the coast of South America around Christmas. El Niño means 'Christ child'. The most intense El Niño event on record occurred in 1982–83 at the time when global temperatures were reaching an all-time record high (1983 is the second warmest year globally on record). The event brought severe storms and floods to South America in its dry season. Australia suffered one of the worst droughts in living memory, which devastated livestock and scorched the land. The cold nutrient waters off the coast of South America were replaced with warm currents lacking in nutrients, with the result that the fishing industry completely failed that year. So sea currents can change direction, they may be linked to global warming, and they certainly affect the climate. If the Gulf Stream failed, say because global warming changed the salinity gradient of the Atlantic Ocean, then Britain and northern Europe could see substantial cooling. This is just one of the many paradoxes possible in a warming world.

The single most important factor in the atmosphere is cloud cover. In the past clouds have always been cited as nature's way of protecting the planet. If the world gets hotter, then more water will evaporate, more clouds will form to block out the sun, and the planet will get colder. Unfortunately it's not that simple. We all know that clouds cool what would otherwise be a warm day, and at night they keep warm what would otherwise be a cold night. That is, there are greenhouse clouds trapping the earth's heat, but there are reflecting clouds throwing the sunshine away to space. The question is, which will win? At the moment globally the greenhouse clouds cause a warming of 30 watts per square metre, while the reflecting clouds lose us 45 watts per square metre. Thus a net cooling is caused by clouds. How this will change in a warmer world is unpredictable, because the greenhouse and the reflecting clouds are typically at different levels in the atmosphere. Some are made of ice, some are made of water, and some are a combination. One sort of cloud could increase in its effect while another could decrease in its opposite effect, so that changes would reinforce rather than cancel.

My best guess would be for extra cooling. My reasoning behind this is that global warming will turn out to be stronger over polar regions and weaker over tropical regions, which means that the temperature contrast from equator

The oceans, by mixing the surface heating with colder waters beneath, may hold back global warming. Britain may see a much delayed greenhouse effect relative to other parts of the world because of the north Atlantic lagging behind.

Britain's climate depends on the behaviour of the Gulf Stream, so any shift of current caused by global warming could have an effect on our weather far greater than the greenhouse effect. The magnitude of the effect might be gauged from the consequences of El Niño events.

El Niño is a warm ocean current that turns up unpredictably every few years in the tropical Pacific Ocean. A warm surge of water moves to pole will decrease. Since it's the strength of the thermal gradient from equator to pole that drives the atmospheric circulations to produce the thickest and highest ice clouds, then global warming should generally decrease the amounts of high ice cloud. That is, it should decrease the greenhouse clouds (high cirrus is particularly good at warming) relative to the lower reflecting clouds. Thus the atmosphere would produce a larger net cooling in response to global warming. The symmetry of this idea is appealing, but there are many ifs and buts along the way.

The most important consequence of changing cloud amounts is the link with sea level rises, probably the most serious problem facing Britain. The link comes about because the ice caps and ice sheets, which might trigger devastating sea level rises in a warmer world, depend for their size on snowfall. For example, simply decreasing global temperature alone would not produce an ice age, for it would decrease snowfall to such an extent that large accumulations of ice could not build up. The growth of ice sheets in low latitudes demands considerable nourishment from cloudy snow-laden skies. In an enhanced greenhouse world, warmed more at the poles than the equator, the weakened activity of the general circulation of the atmosphere should reduce cloud amounts over polar

regions and therefore reduce snowfall. The slowly melting ice sheets would then be free to go on melting, raising sea levels worldwide. The smaller the ice sheets become, the less sunshine is reflected back to space, the more solar heating is taken up by the oceans, and the faster the meltdown accelerates.

As well as the size or extent of the ice sheets we need to know the thickness of the Antarctic ice shelf that is still attached to the bedrock, the thicker the sheet the slower the melt. Even more importantly it is suspected that the Antarctic waters at the ice shelf edge mix with the deep ocean waters, and so would never warm like other waters. Therefore any ice meltdown would be a very slow process. On the other hand, if the ice shelf broke away from the ice frozen to the bedrock of the Antarctic continent, a giant one million square mile iceberg could drift into warmer waters and cause sea levels to rise several metres over a hundred years. What happens in the oceans is clearly more important than used to be thought. As mentioned earlier, perhaps planet earth should be renamed 'planet ocean'. In terms of ability to store up heat, the top 2.5 metres of ocean are equivalent to the entire atmosphere. In terms of unknowns, the bottom 2.5 metres of ocean are equivalent to millions of miles in space.

Left An iceberg. Some scientists think that a warmer world with warmer oceans would evaporate more water vapour to form more clouds, therefore increasing snowfall over the polar regions. However, this means that the ice sheets would grow and rising sea levels would be partly halted.

To predict the future climate of Britain, climatologists invent models that mimic the world's climate systems. This of course is easier said than done. The idea is to put the model, however poor, into the memory of a computer so that the sums that have to be done can at least be done as fast as possible. Speed is essential because in the real world there are so many processes mixed up in so much space over so much time that a whole army of mathematicians working day and night would soon be over-whelmed; reality would overtake their forecasts. It is not possible, at least not in the 1990s, to assemble a climate model so sophisticated that it takes everything into account. Instead rather crude climate models are in operation in centres around the world, and each one is different. Each one gives different predictions. The consensus view is that a doubling of carbon dioxide contamination by 2030 will cause an average global warming of 2°C. However, we must remember that a model is nothing more than a mathematical statement of someone's theory of how things work. In the case of climate models, which are so incredibly complex and yet still nowhere near able to mimic accurately the climate systems, the conclusions taken from the models are by definition flawed.

Even so, continued release of carbon dioxide and other greenhouse gases into the atmosphere throughout the next century must eventually overwhelm natural variability, which was leading to another ice age, and instead produce significant global warming. Models predict that a quadrupling of carbon dioxide levels in the atmosphere will lead to global warming of some 8°C. This alarming warming could be disguised at first by the natural cycle that wants to take the planet towards an ice age, when ice sheets might return to northern Britain and stay for 100,000 years. It is the astronomical, very slow wobble, tilt and spin of the planet that, although hardly noticeable, causes periodic global cooling. Until the intervention of the industrial revolution (and the explosion of population) the world's climate had been cooling

Right Rotting rubbish leaks methane into the air. Methane is a much stronger greenhouse gas that carbon dioxide, fortunately it is not released in the same vast quantities as carbon dioxide.

Left Discarded fridges found on rubbish dumps are lethal in many ways. The most powerful of the greenhouse gases, CFC's, leak from old fridges into the air, again like methane, not in the vast quantities as carbon dioxide.

very slowly over the previous 6000 years, moving towards the next ice age which was expected in one or two millenia. But now global warming looks like winning; this century has seen global warming of a small amount, 0.5°C. However, interestingly the period 1950 to 1975 saw no warming at all, just at the very time when, if global warming is to be believed, there should have been a marked effect owing to the accumulating greenhouse gases. The lesson drawn from this fact is that the climate must have marked natural variability. That is, the 0.5°C warming may be nothing more than natural variability, and the greenhouse effect just a lot of hot air! This is why, despite the 1980s being globally the warmest decade on record, and 1988 being the warmest year of all, scientists still cannot agree for sure that global warming has begun. As suggested in Chapter 3, in the next century we will be able to look back at the 1980s and then perhaps say, 'Yes, that was the first sign.'

Carbon dioxide and water vapour are the most important greenhouse gases, but not the only ones. There are four others:

- Methane, from rotting rubbish, cattle digestion, rotting wood, paddy fields and natural gas before it's burnt.
- Ozone, from the chemical reaction of sunlight on car exhaust fumes.
- Nitrous oxide, mostly from nitrogen-based fertilisers.
- Chlorofluorocarbons (CFCs), mostly from refrigerators and aerosols.

To some extent all these gases intercept earth's cooling radiation and return it to earth. In cooling, the earth radiates a range of wavelengths, not all of which are trapped by water vapour in the air. The apparent hole in the sky to terrestrial radiation is called the 'water vapour window'. Any new absorber placed in this window that blocks the night cooling of the earth can have a strong effect on the temperature of the earth. The relative contributions to the man-made greenhouse effect are: methane 15 per cent, ozone 5 per cent, nitrous oxide 5 per cent, and CFCs 25 per cent.

Right The increasing use of chemical fertilisers will increase the amount of nitrous oxide in the air. Nitrogen based fertilisers need to be cut back.

Right Traffic fumes react with sunlight to produce ozone in the lower atmosphere — another greenhouse gas.

CFCs are powerful greenhouse gases and, although much less pervasive than carbon dioxide, contribute up to 25 per cent to the man-made greenhouse enhancement. CFCs are chlorine-based compounds released from aerosols, foam packaging, refrigerators, air conditioners and industrial solvents. It used to be thought that, like carbon dioxide in the air, CFCs would eventually sink into the ocean. The theory was that CFCs attached themselves to specks of sand and dust in the air, and were eventually rained out – never finding their way into the stratosphere. To everyone's surprise the British Antarctic Survey team discovered that chlorine molecules were finding their way into the strato-sphere – and, what is more, were destroying the

world's ozone shield above the Antarctic. This was confirmed by remote sensing satellites. Great seasonal holes in the ozone layer have developed over the pole. There is also increasing speculation that the entire ozone shield in the stratosphere, which envelops the world, could be destroyed by CFCs.

As well as adding to the greenhouse effect by allowing more solar energy in, any substantial depletion of the ozone layer in the stratosphere would threaten life on earth. The kind of high energy radiation from the sun that would penetrate to earth can kill DNA molecules and cause mutations. This lethal ultraviolet from the sun was originally blocked out on primitive earth by the oceans; therefore life began in the oceans. The living cells fed on carbon compounds and gave off oxygen as waste. Over millions of years oxygen floated upwards from the oceans into the atmosphere and up into the stratosphere, where it reacted with sunlight to form ozone. Once the ozone shield was thick enough to ward off the lethal ultraviolet rays from the sun, life crawled out from the water's edge on to the land. This changed the planet's surface from bald and reflective to dark and absorbing. In turn, this stopped the hostile wild swing of temperature from day to night. The greenhouse gases erupting from the fiery interior of the earth, and held to earth by gravity, kept average global temperatures above freezing.

In this way climate and life coevolved on earth. We depend on climate for continued life on earth and the climate depends on what life does on earth. The great British obsession with climate and weather is just part of a worldwide concern – a concern that the world's climate cannot just be taken for granted. There is a big price to pay for dumping pollution into our atmosphere and changing the climate on which we all depend. At the moment the 'free market' is rigged in favour of those who add more and more greenhouse gases to the air. The burning of coal, oil, gas and so on is necessary for our modern way of life, but when compared with alternative energy sources the true cost is far greater than simply the quoted price of the raw materials. In the case of CFCs this idea has been taken on board by many governments, and alternative 'ozone friendly' substitutes have been found. What is needed now are 'climate friendly' energy sources.

There are however some hopeful rays through the clouds of uncertainty that shroud our climate's future. The three main contentious issues – global warming, ozone depletion and acid rain – are all now regarded as real problems that have to be tackled.

Governments are traditionally quite weary of pressure groups that seem to jump to alarmist conclusions from little research and even less tangible evidence. For example, on the 3rd of August 1990, the temperature reached a record of 37.1°C around Cheltenham. Could this have been another sign of the greenhouse effect? No one knows. However, with the help of the mass media, if there is a good case well argued people always take note. For example the Campaign Against Lead In Petrol (CALIP) started in the 1970s when some parents discovered their children had high lead blood counts and were hyperactive. At first the government deflected the protests round the Department of the Environment, the Ministry of Transport and the Treasury. Arguments against action like 'cars cannot run on lead free petrol', and 'the children must have swallowed lead paint at school' were employed at first. CALIP took all the petrol industry's points in turn and eventually won the argument.

Today the British Government has accepted the case for ozone depletion and has played a leading role in getting 59 nations plus India and China (who account for more than a third of mankind) to agree to phase out all CFCs by the year 2000. This excellent achievement bodes well for our future.

Another good sign is that on the acid rain front the CEGB is funding extensive research into the sulphur cycle. The cost of fitting scrubbers to coal power stations is enormous, whereas cheap electricity is vital to Britain. Some suggest switching from coal to nuclear power over the next few decades, because nuclear is a relatively clean fuel that would cut acid rain and cut carbon dioxide emission (the main cause of global warming).

Globally, if CFCs were phased out and their substitutes not greenhouse gases, and if there was a major energy switch to nuclear power, then the concentration of greenhouse gases in the atmosphere would actually fall. The only problem is that nobody wants a nuclear power station in their back yard.

The United Nations Intergovernmental Panel on Climate Change is trying to assess global warming and its impact on us all. The reports of the Panel show that the problem is a real one, but that the solutions are uncertain.

THE GREAT BRITISH OBSESSION

What can be stated is that the cause of the greenhouse effect is not just coal or cars or cutting down forests but a whole range of man's activities. The solutions will therefore have to be global. Everyone can help. Each individual effort on its own, will of course seem insignificant, but when multiplied millions of times the effect is considerable. The main drive must be to reduce energy consumption, and that's anything from more efficient lights to less use of cars. Nearly all energy conservation ideas are good for their own sake, and after all we could all end up with smaller bills and fitter bodies.

On the other hand, it is true that the future climate cannot be predicted with confidence: so maybe all action on pollution can just wait for more certainty? That is a slippery slope, a short-sighted way of looking at things. If the wheels are still turning, and at some time in the future it is deemed necessary to slam the brakes on greenhouse emissions, then we may lock the wheels but the sheer inertia will slide us all for another century into a future that nobody wants. The great dilemma may be only half a century away.

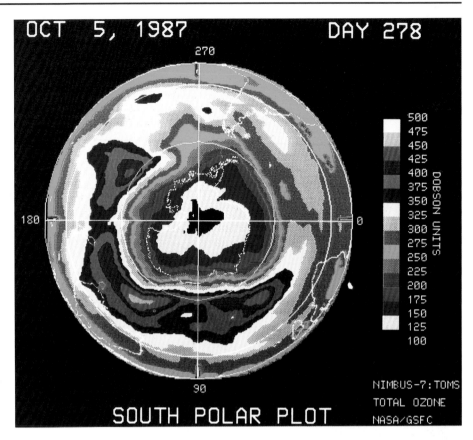

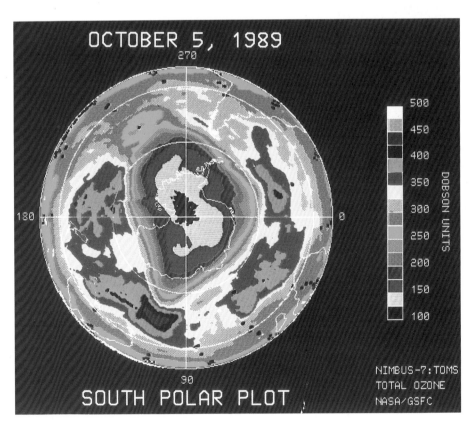

Right NASA satellite measurements of ozone concentrations in the stratosphere show great holes over the Antarctic in October. The lowest recorded ozone level, less than 100 Dobson units, was in 1987 and the hole was again there in 1989. The ozone shield is extremely important, as it protects us from the harmful ultraviolet rays.

ILL MET BY SUNLIGHT

There was this lecturer speaking on the end of the world, which will happen in five thousand million years, when the sun becomes vaster and vaster until its swirling volume actually balloons out to engulf the innermost planets, scorching the rest with its unbelievable . . .

At this point in the lecture, a man in the front row begins screaming and foaming at the mouth, babbling about 'Death and destruction! *Death* and destruction!'

'It's all right,' says the lecturer, patting him on the cheek, 'it's not for another five thousand million years.'

'Thank God for that,' says the man, sitting up and straightening his tie, 'I thought you said *four* thousand million years.'

Jonathan Sale, *Punch*

Index

Acknowledgements

Many thanks to the following photographers and picture libraries. The pictures are numbered from left to right and top to bottom on the page.

8, 13(1) Patrick Eagar. 9 Tate Gallery, London. 10 The Kobal Collection. 11(1) & (2), 37, 48, 51, 98, 99, 108(1), 109, 110(1), 112, 113(1), 116(2) & (3), 132 Robin Chittenden/RB Photo Library. 13(2) & (3), 58/59 Professional Sports. 15(1) Eric Whitehead Photography. 15(2) David E Reid c/o Alex Davis. 16, 82, 84(2) National Maritime Museum. 17, 18, 19(1), 50(1) & (2), 55, 78, 79, 126 Mary Evans Picture Library. 19(2) Camera Press Limited. 20(2), 124 Clive Byers. 21 Collin Andrews. 22, 23, 24, 34, 41, 56(1), (2) & (3), 57, 65, 119, 130(2) Eastern Daily Press. 25 Mike Thomas. 26(2) H Binz. 3 Western Morning News. 68 A Wharton. 69 K Garni. 72, 73(1) & (2) Mark Thomas, 106 R Thompson, 129(1) Mark Newman – Frank Lane Picture Agency. 28 P J Garner. 28 Douglas Volz. 29(1) P Fitzgerald. 29(2) Paul McKillop. 30 Hans Heinrich Schiesser. 32, 60, 69(3), 135 Robert Estall. 36, 110(2) Tony Lake. 38(1) & (2) North Yorkshire County Library. 39(1) Hampshire County Library. 39(2) Bognor Regis History Society. 44 Piers Cavendish/Reflex. 53, 97(1) R K Pilsbury. 61 Royal Botanical Gardens, Kew. 62, 63 Wokingham Times. 64 'The News', Portsmouth. 64(2), 83(1), 84(2) Crown Copyright reproduced with permission of HMSO. 80(2) Denis Avon. 67 B. White. 75 Blackpool Evening Gazette. 82(1) J. Galvin. 84 N Elkins. 85, 128 Science Photo Library. 64, 76, 88, 89 Department of Electrical Engineering, Dundee University. 90, 91, 92 BBC's Photographic Library. 93 K Allsop. 96 William Warwick. 97(2) Karen Heywood. 100 M Nimmo. 103 Royal Meteorological Society. 102, 103 Alistair McHardy. 104(1) R K Pilsbury (2) J Galvin (3) Stephen Burt (4) A Gair (5) J Houseman (6) P Nye (7) K Woodley (8) Robin Chittenden (9) J Walton (10) R Russel. 108(2) Kim Taylor/Bruce Colman Limited. 113(2) Raymond Sacks. 114 Greenpeace/Zindler. 115(1) Greenpeace/Kerr. 115(2) Malcolm Thomson. 117 A Holding. 118 A Perkins. 120 W Cunnington. 121 NASA. 124(2), (3) & (4) Greenpeace/Plowden. 131(1) & (2) Hulton Picture Library. 134 Stephen Burt. 138(1) British Agrochemicals Association Limited. 140 NASA. 141 M Cairns.

Special thanks are due to those organisations that have contributed heavily to this book. They are – Punch Publications Limited, The National Meteorological Library and its staff, Robin Chittenden/RB Photo Library, Piers Millington-Wallace for his illustrations and Georgina Harris for her maps.

Many thanks to Jaqueline Karas, Senior Research Assistant at the Climatic Research Unit of UEA, for her expert knowledge. Thanks also to Caroline Rose and Sarah Gates for their keyboard skills.

Every effort has been made to obtain the appropriate rights or permission to publish all copyright material. The publishers would be pleased to acknowledge any omission in future editions.

Pictures *prelim pages* (left to right)
W Cunnington
Tony Lake
Robin Chittenden
R K Pilsbury
Robin Chittenden
K Allsopp